HEATH
MIDDLE LEVEL
LITERATURE

Strange and Special Places

A place can be important for many different reasons.
Strange and special places should be treasured and
protected. Do you have such a place?

A U T H O R S

Donna Alvermann
Linda Miller Cleary
Kenneth Donelson
Donald Gallo
Alice Haskins
J. Howard Johnston
John Lounsbury
Alleen Pace Nilsen
Robert Pavlik
Jewell Parker Rhodes
Alberto Alvaro Ríos
Sandra Schurr
Lyndon Searfoss
Julia Thomason
Max Thompson
Carl Zon

D.C. Heath and Company
Lexington, Massachusetts / Toronto, Ontario

STAFF CREDITS

EDITORIAL	Barbara A. Brennan, Marjorie Glazer, Christopher Johnson, Peg McNary, Lalia Nuzzolo, Rita M. Sullivan
	Proofreading: JoAnne B. Sgroi
CONTRIBUTING WRITERS	Carol Domblewski, Lisa Moore
SERIES DESIGN	Robin Herr
BOOK DESIGN	Caroline Bowden, Daniel Derdula, Susan Geer, Diana Maloney, Angela Sciaraffa, Bonnie Chayes Yousefian
	Art Editing: Carolyn Langley
PHOTOGRAPHY	*Series Photography Coordinator:* Carmen Johnson
	Photo Research Supervisor: Martha Friedman
	Photo Researchers: Wendy Enright, Po-yee McKenna, PhotoSearch, Inc., Gillian Speeth, Denise Theodores
	Assignment Photography Coordinators: Susan Doheny, Gayna Hoffman, Shawna Johnston
COMPUTER PREPRESS	Ricki Pappo, Kathy Meisl, Richard Curran, Michele Locatelli
PERMISSIONS	Dorothy B. McLeod
PRODUCTION	Patrick Connolly

Cover Painting: © William Lesch, SWANSTOCK. **Cover Design:** Diane Levy

International Standard Book Number: 0-669-32090-0
1 2 3 4 5 6 7 8 9 10-RRD- 99 98 97 96 95 94

Middle Level Authors

Donna Alvermann, University of Georgia
Alice Haskins, Howard County Public Schools, Maryland
J. Howard Johnston, University of South Florida
John Lounsbury, Georgia College
Sandra Schurr, University of South Florida
Julia Thomason, Appalachian State University
Max Thompson, Appalachian State University
Carl Zon, California Assessment Collaborative

Literature and Language Arts Authors

Linda Miller Cleary, University of Minnesota
Kenneth Donelson, Arizona State University
Donald Gallo, Central Connecticut State University
Alleen Pace Nilsen, Arizona State University
Robert Pavlik, Cardinal Stritch College, Milwaukee
Jewell Parker Rhodes, California State University, Northridge
Alberto Alvaro Ríos, Arizona State University
Lyndon Searfoss, Arizona State University

Teacher Consultants

Suzanne Aubin, Patapsco Middle School, Ellicott City, Maryland
Judy Baxter, Newport News Public Schools, Newport News, Virginia
Saundra Bryn, Director of Research and Development, El Mirage, Arizona
Lorraine Gerhart, Elmbrook Middle School, Elm Grove, Wisconsin
Kathy Tuchman Glass, Burlingame Intermediate School, Burlingame, California
Lucretia Pannozzo, John Jay Middle School, Katonah, New York
Carol Schultz, Jerling Junior High, Orland Park, Illinois
Jeanne Siebenman, Grand Canyon University, Phoenix, Arizona
Gail Thompson, Garey High School, Pomona, California
Rufus Thompson, Grace Yokley School, Ontario, California
Tom Tufts, Conniston Middle School, West Palm Beach, Florida
Edna Turner, Harpers Choice Middle School, Columbia, Maryland
C. Anne Webb, Buerkle Junior High School, St. Louis, Missouri
Geri Yaccino, Thompson Junior High School, St. Charles, Illinois

CONTENTS

THE LITERATURE

ASKING BIG QUESTIONS ABOUT THE LITERATURE

OUR OWN
SPECIAL PLACES

Close your eyes and think about one of your favorite places. Maybe it's the space under your basement stairs or the clubhouse where you and your friends sometimes meet. Here's a game that will help you see the variety of places that are special to you and your classmates. First, divide your class into several teams of four or six members and get ready to play a game called GUESS WHERE!

1
Think about your favorite places.

On a slip of paper, write your name, a favorite place, and at least five sensory details of that place. Such details are words and phrases that appeal to one of the senses. Therefore, try to think of a sight, a sound, a smell, a taste, and a touch that are particular to the place you have chosen. Be as specific as you can. Here's an example.

OUR SUMMER CAMPSITE
SIGHT: golden morning light
SOUND: water lapping on rocks
SMELL: fresh pine needles
TASTE: sweet dried fruits
TOUCH: cool damp soil

2 Guess where!

Look at your list of details and circle the three you think are the best. Then eliminate any details that you think will automatically give away your place.

TO PLAY: Have two teams sit together. To start, a member from Team A chooses one detail and calls on a volunteer from Team B to guess what the special place might be. For example, if "salty popcorn" is the clue, the guess might be "basketball game." If Team B guesses incorrectly, the Team A member gives another clue and calls on a new volunteer from Team B. Team A scores a point for each clue that is not correctly identified. If Team B correctly guesses the place, it scores a point. Members of both teams take turns giving clues and guessing until everyone has had a turn.

3 Everyone wins.

After everyone has had a chance to share his or her special place, tally the score. But remember, everyone wins at this game because it's made you think about all the different places that are special to your classmates.

Asking Big Questions About the Theme

? What are some favorite places people have?

If you could be somewhere else, where would you be? Close your eyes and picture the place in as much detail as you can. Imagine the sights, smells, and sounds. Is it hot or cold? Windy or still? Noisy or quiet? What is close by and farther away? Then, in your journal, write a description of the place. Include colors, sensations, feelings, sizes, shapes, textures—any details that will make the place come alive. Finally, read over the description and circle your favorite details.

? What makes a place special?

What's the best place you've been to recently? What's the worst? In your journal, make webs like the ones shown that give details about each place. Then find two magazine photographs that remind you of the best and worst places. Share them with your classmates along with reasons for your choices. Combine your photos with your classmates' photos to make a collage of good and bad places.

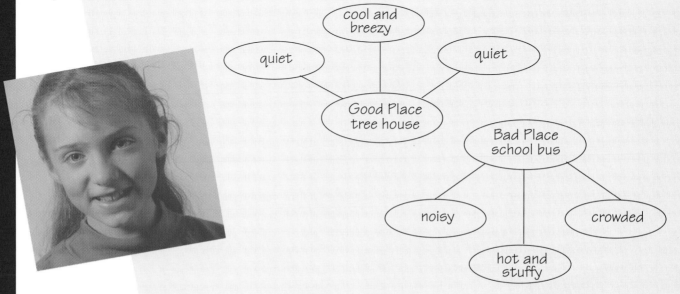

cool and breezy

quiet

quiet

Good Place tree house

Bad Place school bus

noisy

crowded

hot and stuffy

Why do people seek strange and special places?

People may seek strange and special places for reasons such as curiosity, excitement, or privacy. With a partner, choose a place and design a magazine advertisement for it. Brainstorm sensory details that will attract people to the place. Then write a phrase that will appear in large bold type in your advertisement. What photograph or drawing will you include in your ad? What other **copy,** or words, will you use? Display your ad on a bulletin board.

How do people react to strange and special places?

By yourself, with a partner, or with your whole class, brainstorm a list of at least ten words of emotion—such as *FEAR, EXCITEMENT,* and *AWE.* Use a dictionary or thesaurus to help you. Then, in your journal, create a chart like the one shown. For each emotion, write down a place that makes you feel it. For example, does a dark room make you feel FEAR? Save your list for future reference.

FEAR	dark room
EXCITEMENT	the pool at swim meets
AWE	the Egyptian Room at the museum
JOY	
SADNESS	

NOW

Think!

As you read the selections, think about the strange and special places that you already know and the places that you might visit someday. In real life, your choices might be limited, but in literature, there are no limits at all. And now, take a deep breath and turn the page. You're off to new places that writers have created with words.

UNDER
THE
BACK
PORCH

VIRGINIA HAMILTON

Our house is two stories high
shaped like a white box.
There is a yard stretched around it
and in back
a wooden porch.   5

Under the back porch is my place.
I rest there.
I go there when I have to be alone.
It is always shaded and damp.
Sunlight only slants through the slats   10
in long strips of light,
and the smell of the damp
is moist green,
like the moss that grows here.

My sisters and brothers   15
can stand on the back porch
and never know
I am here
underneath.
It is my place.   20
All mine.

VIRGINIA HAMILTON

Virginia Hamilton was born in 1936 in Yellow Springs, Ohio, where her family has lived for several generations. When a person has known a town for all her life, she is likely to think of one small spot there as a special place.

Rulers of Terabithia

from

Bridge to Terabithia

KATHERINE PATERSON

Because school had started on the first Tuesday after Labor Day, it was a short week. It was a good thing because each day was worse than the one before. Leslie continued to join the boys at recess, and every day she won. By Friday a number of the fourth- and fifth-grade boys had already drifted away to play King of the Mountain on the slope between the two fields. Since there were only a handful left, they didn't even have to have heats, which took away a lot of the suspense. Running wasn't fun anymore. And it was all Leslie's fault.

Jess knew now that he would never be the best runner of the fourth and fifth grades, and his only consolation was that neither would Gary Fulcher. They went through the motions of the contest on Friday, but when it was over and Leslie had won again, everyone sort of knew without saying so that it was the end of the races.

At least it was Friday, and Miss Edmunds was back. The fifth grade had music right after recess. Jess had passed Miss Edmunds in the hall earlier in the day and she had stopped him and made a fuss over him. "Did you keep drawing this summer?"

"Yes'm."

"May I see your pictures or are they private?"

Jess shoved his hair off his red forehead. "I'll show you 'um."

She smiled her beautiful even-toothed smile and shook her shining black hair back off her shoulders. "Great!" she said. "See you."

He nodded and smiled back. Even his toes had felt warm and tingly.

Now as he sat on the rug in the teachers' room the same warm feeling swept through him at the sound of her voice. Even her ordinary speaking voice bubbled up from inside her, rich and melodic.

Miss Edmunds fiddled a minute with her guitar, talking as she tightened the strings to the jingling of her bracelets and the thrumming of chords. She was in her jeans as usual and sat there cross-legged in front of them as though that was the way teachers always did. She asked a few of the kids how they were and how their summer had been. They kind of mumbled back. She didn't speak directly to Jess, but she gave him a look with those blue eyes of hers that made him zing like one of the strings she was strumming.

She took note of Leslie and asked for an introduction, which one of the girls prissily[1] gave. Then she smiled at Leslie, and Leslie smiled back—the first time Jess could remember seeing Leslie smile since she won the race on Tuesday. "What do you like to sing, Leslie?"

"Oh, anything."

Miss Edmunds picked a few odd chords and then began to sing, more quietly than usual for that particular song:

> *"I see a land bright and clear*
> *And the time's coming near*
> *When we'll live in this land*
> *You and me, hand in hand . . ."*

People began to join in, quietly at first to match her mood, but as the song built up at the end, their voices did as well, so that by the time they got to the final "Free to be you and me," the whole school could hear them. Caught in the pure delight of it, Jess turned and his eyes met Leslie's. He smiled at her. What the heck? There wasn't any reason he couldn't. What was he scared of anyhow? Lord. Sometimes he acted like the original yellow-bellied sapsucker. He nodded and smiled again. She smiled back. He felt there in the teachers' room that it was the beginning of a new season in his life, and he chose deliberately to make it so.

He did not have to make any announcement to Leslie that he had changed his mind about her. She already knew it. She plunked

---

1. **prissily** [pris′ sə lē]: too nicely.

herself down beside him on the bus and squeezed over closer to him to make room for May Belle on the same seat. She talked about Arlington, about the huge suburban school she used to go to with its gorgeous music room but not a single teacher in it as beautiful or as nice as Miss Edmunds.

"You had a gym?"

"Yeah. I think all the schools did. Or most of them anyway." She sighed. "I really miss it. I'm pretty good at gymnastics."

"I guess you hate it here."

"Yeah."

She was quiet for a moment, thinking, Jess decided, about her former school, which he saw as bright and new with a gleaming gymnasium larger than the one at the consolidated[2] high school.

"I guess you had a lot of friends there, too."

"Yeah."

"Why'd you come here?"

"My parents are reassessing their value structure."

"Huh?"

"They decided they were too hooked on money and success, so they bought that old farm and they're going to farm it and think about what's important."

Jess was staring at her with his mouth open. He knew it, and he couldn't help himself. It was the most ridiculous thing he had ever heard.

"But you're the one that's gotta pay."

"Yeah."

"Why don't they think about you?"

"We talked it over," she explained patiently. "I wanted to come, too." She looked past him out the window. "You never know ahead of time what something's really going to be like."

The bus had stopped. Leslie took May Belle's hand and led her off. Jess followed, still trying to figure out why two grown people and a smart girl like Leslie wanted to leave a comfortable life in the suburbs for a place like this.

2. **consolidated** [kən sol′ ə dāt əd]: many combined into one.

They watched the bus roar off.

"You can't make a go of a farm nowadays, you know," he said finally. "My dad has to go to Washington to work, or we wouldn't have enough money . . ."

"Money is not the problem."

"Sure it's the problem."

"I mean," she said stiffly, "not for us."

It took him a minute to catch on. He did not know people for whom money was not the problem. "Oh." He tried to remember not to talk about money with her after that.

But Leslie had other problems at Lark Creek that caused more of a rumpus[3] than lack of money. There was the matter of television.

It started with Mrs. Myers reading out loud a composition that Leslie had written about her hobby. Everyone had had to write a paper about his or her favorite hobby. Jess had written about football, which he really hated, but he had enough brains to know that if he said drawing, everyone would laugh at him. Most of the boys swore that watching the Washington Redskins on TV was their favorite hobby. The girls were divided: those who didn't care much about what Mrs. Myers thought chose watching game shows on TV, and those like Wanda Kay Moore who were still aiming for A's chose reading Good Books. But Mrs. Myers didn't read anyone's paper out loud except Leslie's.

"I want to read this composition aloud. For two reasons. One, it is *beautifully* written. And two, it tells about an unusual hobby—for a girl." Mrs. Myers beamed her first-day smile at Leslie. Leslie stared at her desk. Being Mrs. Myers' pet was pure poison at Lark Creek. "'Scuba Diving' by Leslie Burke."

Mrs. Myers' sharp voice cut Leslie's sentences into funny little phrases, but even so, the power of Leslie's words drew Jess with her under the dark water. Suddenly he could hardly breathe. Suppose you went under and your mask filled all up with water and you couldn't get to the top in time? He was choking and sweating. He tried to push down his panic. This was Leslie Burke's favorite hobby. Nobody

3. **rumpus** [rum′ pəs]: a noisy disturbance.

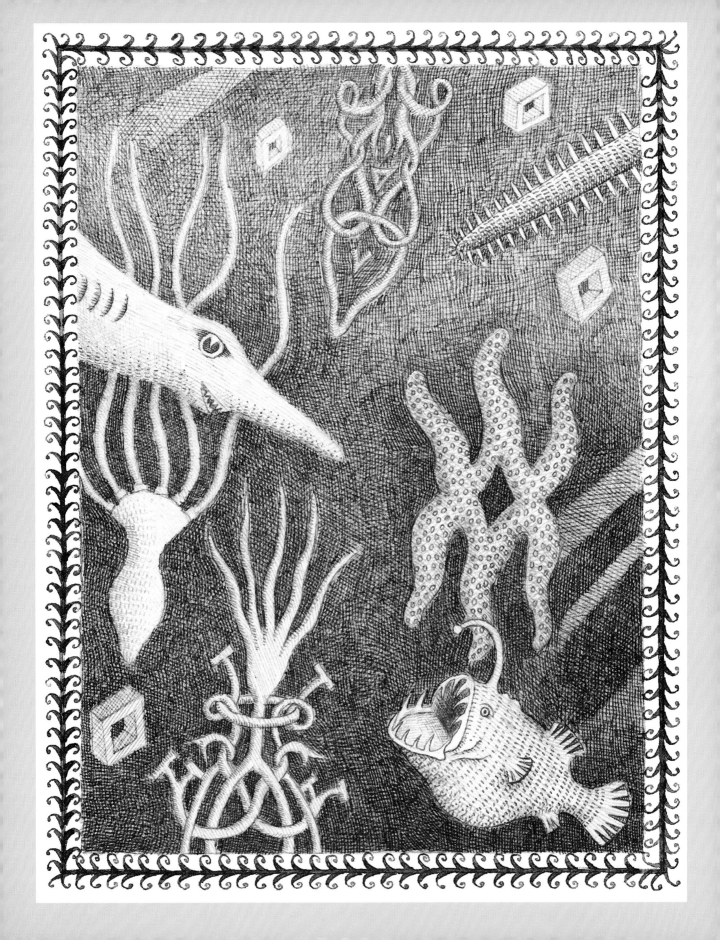

would make up scuba diving to be their favorite hobby if it wasn't so. That meant Leslie did it a lot. That she wasn't scared of going deep, deep down in a world of no air and little light. Lord, he was such a coward. How could he be all in a tremble just listening to Mrs. Myers read about it? He was worse a baby than Joyce Ann. His dad expected him to be a man. And here he was letting some girl who wasn't even ten yet scare the liver out of him by just telling what it was like to sight-see under water. Dumb, dumb, dumb.

"I am sure," Mrs. Myers was saying, "that all of you were as impressed as I was with Leslie's exciting essay."

Impressed. Lord. He'd nearly drowned.

In the classroom there was a shuffling of feet and papers. "Now I want to give you a homework assignment"—muffled groans—"that I'm sure you'll enjoy."—mumblings of unbelief—"Tonight on Channel 7 at 8 P.M. there is going to be a special about a famous underwater explorer—Jacques Cousteau. I want everyone to watch. Then write one page telling what you learned."

"A whole page?"

"Yes."

"Does spelling count?"

"Doesn't spelling always count, Gary?"

"Both sides of the paper?"

"One side will be enough, Wanda Kay. But I will give extra credit to those who do extra work."

Wanda Kay smiled primly. You could already see ten pages taking shape in her pointy head.

"Mrs. Myers."

"Yes. Leslie." Lord, Mrs. Myers was liable to crack her face if she kept up smiling like that.

"What if you can't watch the program?"

"You inform your parents that it is a homework assignment. I am sure they will not object."

"What if"—Leslie's voice faltered; then she shook her head and cleared her throat so the words came out stronger—"what if you don't have a television set?"

Lord, Leslie. Don't say that. You can always watch on mine. But it was too late to save her. The hissing sounds of disbelief were already building into a rumbling of contempt.

Mrs. Myers blinked her eyes. "Well. Well." She blinked some more. You could tell she was trying to figure out how to save Leslie, too. "Well. In that case one could write a one-page composition on something else. Couldn't one, Leslie?" She tried to smile across the classroom upheaval to Leslie, but it was no use. "Class! Class! *Class!*" Her Leslie smile shifted suddenly and ominously[4] into a scowl that silenced the storm.

She handed out dittoed sheets of arithmetic problems. Jess stole a look at Leslie. Her face, bent low over the math sheet, was red and fierce.

At recess time when he was playing King of the Mountain, he could see that Leslie was surrounded by a group of girls led by Wanda Kay. He couldn't hear what they were saying, but he could tell by the proud way Leslie was throwing her head back that the others were making fun of her. Greg Williams grabbed him then, and while they wrestled, Leslie disappeared. It was none of his business, really, but he threw Greg down the hill as hard as he could and yelled to no one in particular, "Gotta go."

He stationed himself across from the girls' room. Leslie came out in a few minutes. He could tell she had been crying.

"Hey, Leslie," he called softly.

"Go away!" She turned abruptly and headed the other way in a fast walk. With an eye on the office door, he ran after her. Nobody was supposed to be in the halls during recess. "Leslie. Whatsa matter?"

"You know perfectly well what's the matter, Jess Aarons."

"Yeah." He rubbed his hair. "If you'd justa kept your mouth shut. You can always watch at my . . ."

But she had wheeled around again, and was zooming down the hall. Before he could finish the sentence and catch up with her, she

4. **ominously** [om′ ə nəs lē]: threateningly.

was swinging the door to the girls' room right at his nose. Jess slunk out of the building. He couldn't risk Mr. Turner catching him hanging around the girls' room as though he was some kind of pervert or something.

After school Leslie got on the bus before he did and went straight to the corner of the long back seat—right to the seventh graders' seat. He jerked his head at her to warn her to come farther up front, but she wouldn't even look at him. He could see the seventh graders headed for the bus—the huge bossy bosomy girls and the mean, skinny, narrow-eyed boys. They'd kill her for sitting in their territory. He jumped up and ran to the back and grabbed Leslie by the arm. "You gotta come up to your regular seat, Leslie."

Even as he spoke, he could feel the bigger kids pushing up behind him down the narrow aisle. Indeed, Janice Avery, who among all the seventh graders was the one person who devoted her entire life to scaring the wits out of anyone smaller than she, was right behind him. "Move, kid," she said.

He planted his body as firmly as he could, although his heart was knocking at his Adam's apple. "C'mon, Leslie," he said, and then he made himself turn and give Janice Avery one of those look-overs from frizz blond hair, past too tight blouse and broad-beamed jeans, to gigantic sneakers. When he finished, he swallowed, stared straight up into her scowling face, and said, almost steadily, "Don't look like there'll be room across the back here for you *and* Janice Avery."

Somebody hooted. "Weight Watchers is waiting for you, Janice!"

Janice's eyes were hate-mad, but she moved aside for Jess and Leslie to make their way past her to their regular seat.

Leslie glanced back as they sat down, and then leaned over. "She's going to get you for that, Jess. Boy, she is mad."

Jess warmed to the tone of respect in Leslie's voice, but he didn't dare look back. "Heck," he said. "You think I'm going to let some dumb cow like that scare me?"

By the time they got off the bus, he could finally send a swallow past his Adam's apple without choking. He even gave a little wave at the back seat as the bus pulled off.

Leslie was grinning at him over May Belle's head.

"Well," he said happily. "See you."

"Hey, do you think we could do something this afternoon?"

"Me, too! I wanna do something, too," May Belle shrilled.

Jess looked at Leslie. No was in her eyes. "Not this time, May Belle. Leslie and I got something we gotta do just by ourselves today. You can carry my books home and tell Momma I'm over at Burkes'. OK?"

"You ain't got nothing to do. You ain't even planned nothing."

Leslie came and leaned over May Belle, putting her hand on the little girl's thin shoulder. "May Belle, would you like some new paper dolls?"

May Belle slid her eyes around suspiciously. "What kind?"

"Life in Colonial America."

May Belle shook her head. "I want Bride or Miss America."

"You can pretend these are bride paper dolls. They have lots of beautiful long dresses."

"Whatsa matter with 'um?"

"Nothing. They're brand-new."

"How come you don't want 'um if they're so great?"

"When you're my age"—Leslie gave a little sigh—"you just don't play with paper dolls anymore. My grandmother sent me these. You know how it is, grandmothers just forget you're growing up."

May Belle's one living grandmother was in Georgia and never sent her anything. "You already punched 'um out?"

"No, honestly. And all the clothes punch out, too. You don't have to use scissors."

They could see she was weakening. "How about," Jess began, "you coming down and taking a look at 'um, and if they suit you, you could take 'um along home when you go tell Momma where I am?"

After they had watched May Belle tearing up the hill, clutching her new treasure, Jess and Leslie turned and ran up over the empty field behind the old Perkins place and down to the dry creek bed that separated farmland from the woods. There was an old crab apple tree there, just at the bank of the creek bed, from which someone long forgotten had hung a rope.

They took turns swinging across the gully on the rope. It was a glorious autumn day, and if you looked up as you swung, it gave you the feeling of floating. Jess leaned back and drank in the rich, clear color of the sky. He was drifting, drifting like a fat white lazy cloud back and forth across the blue.

"Do you know what we need?" Leslie called to him. Intoxicated as he was with the heavens, he couldn't imagine needing anything on earth.

"We need a place," she said, "just for us. It would be so secret that we would never tell anyone in the whole world about it." Jess came swinging back and dragged his feet to stop. She lowered her voice almost to a whisper. "It might be a whole secret country," she continued, "and you and I would be the rulers of it."

Her words stirred inside of him. He'd like to be a ruler of something. Even something that wasn't real. "OK," he said. "Where could we have it?"

"Over there in the woods where nobody would come and mess it up."

There were parts of the woods that Jess did not like. Dark places where it was almost like being under water, but he didn't say so.

"I know"—she was getting excited—"it could be a magic country like Narnia,[5] and the only way you can get in is by swinging across on this enchanted rope." Her eyes were bright. She grabbed the rope. "Come on," she said. "Let's find a place to build our castle stronghold."

They had gone only a few yards into the woods beyond the creek bed when Leslie stopped.

"How about right here?" she asked.

"Sure," Jess agreed quickly, relieved that there was no need to plunge deeper into the woods. He would take her there, of course, for he wasn't such a coward that he would mind a little exploring now and then farther in amongst the ever-darkening columns of the tall

5. **Narnia** [när′ nya]: a mythical place in *The Chronicles of Narnia* by C.S. Lewis.

pines. But as a regular thing, as a permanent place, this was where he would choose to be—here where the dogwood and redbud played hide and seek between the oaks and evergreens, and the sun flung itself in golden streams through the trees to splash warmly at their feet.

"Sure," he repeated himself, nodding vigorously. The underbrush was dry and would be easy to clear away. The ground was almost level. "This'll be a good place to build."

Leslie named their secret land "Terabithia,"[6] and she loaned Jess all of her books about Narnia, so he would know how things went in a magic kingdom—how the animals and the trees must be protected and how a ruler must behave. That was the hard part. When Leslie spoke, the words rolling out so regally, you knew she was a proper queen. He could hardly manage English, much less the poetic language of a king.

But he could make stuff. They dragged boards and other materials down from the scrap heap by Miss Bessie's pasture and built their castle stronghold in the place they had found in the woods. Leslie filled a three-pound coffee can with crackers and dried fruit and a one-pound can with strings and nails. They found five old Pepsi bottles which they washed and filled with water, in case, as Leslie said, "of siege."

Like God in the Bible, they looked at what they had made and found it very good.

"You should draw a picture of Terabithia for us to hang in the castle," Leslie said.

"I can't." How could he explain it in a way Leslie would understand, how he yearned to reach out and capture the quivering life about him and how when he tried, it slipped past his fingertips, leaving a dry fossil upon the page? "I just can't get the poetry of the trees," he said.

She nodded. "Don't worry," she said. "You will someday."

He believed her because there in the shadowy light of the stronghold everything seemed possible. Between the two of them

6. **Terabithia** [tār ə bith′ yä]

they owned the world and no enemy, Gary Fulcher, Wanda Kay Moore, Janice Avery, Jess's own fears and insufficiencies, nor any of the foes whom Leslie imagined attacking Terabithia, could ever really defeat them.

A few days after they finished the castle, Janice Avery fell down in the school bus and yelled that Jess had tripped her as she went past. She made such a fuss that Mrs. Prentice, the driver, ordered Jess off the bus, and he had to walk the three miles home.

When Jess finally got to Terabithia, Leslie was huddled next to one of the cracks below the roof trying to get enough light to read. There was a picture on the cover which showed a killer whale attacking a dolphin.

"Whatcha doing?" He came in and sat beside her on the ground.

"Reading. I had to do something. That girl!" Her anger came rocketing to the surface.

"It don't matter. I don't mind walking all that much." What was a little hike compared to what Janice Avery might have chosen to do?

"It's the *principle* of the thing, Jess. That's what you've got to understand. You have to stop people like that. Otherwise they turn into tyrants and dictators."

He reached over and took the whale book from her hands, pretending to study the bloody picture on the jacket. "Getting any good ideas?"

"What?"

"I thought you was getting some ideas on how to stop Janice Avery."

"No, stupid. We're trying to *save* the whales. They might become extinct."

He gave her back the book. "You save the whales and shoot the people, huh?"

She grinned finally. "Something like that, I guess. Say, did you ever hear the story about Moby Dick?"

"Who's that?"

"Well, there was once this huge white whale named Moby Dick. . . ."

And Leslie began to spin out a wonderful story about a whale and a crazy sea captain who was bent on killing it. His fingers itched to try to draw it on paper. Maybe if he had some proper paints, he could do it. There ought to be a way of making the whale shimmering white against the dark water.

At first they avoided each other during school hours, but by October they grew careless about their friendship. Gary Fulcher, like Brenda, took great pleasure in teasing Jess about his "*girl* friend." It hardly bothered Jess. He knew that a *girl* friend was somebody who chased you on the playground and tried to grab you and kiss you. He could no more imagine Leslie chasing a boy than he could imagine Mrs. Double-Chinned Myers shinnying up the flagpole. Gary Fulcher could go to you-know-where and warm his toes.

There was really no free time at school except recess, and now that there were no races, Jess and Leslie usually looked for a quiet place on the field, and sat and talked. Except for the magic half hour on Fridays, recess was all that Jess looked forward to at school. Leslie could always come up with something funny that made the long days bearable. Often the joke was on Mrs. Myers. Leslie was one of those people who sat quietly at her desk, never whispering or daydreaming or chewing gum, doing beautiful schoolwork, and yet her brain was so full of mischief that if the teacher could have once seen through that mask of perfection, she would have thrown her out in horror.

Jess could hardly keep a straight face in class just trying to imagine what might be going on behind that angelic look of Leslie's. One whole morning, as Leslie had related it at recess, she had spent imagining Mrs. Myers on one of those fat farms down in Arizona. In her fantasy, Mrs. Myers was one of the foodaholics who would hide bits of candy bars in odd places—up the hot water faucet!—only to be found out and publicly humiliated before all the other fat ladies. That afternoon Jess kept having visions of Mrs. Myers dressed only in a pink corset being weighed in. "You've been cheating again, Gussie!" the tall skinny directoress was saying. Mrs. Myers was on the verge of tears.

"Jesse Aarons!" The teacher's sharp voice punctured his day-dream. He couldn't look Mrs. Myers straight in her pudgy face. He'd crack up. He set his sight on her uneven hemline.

"Yes'm." He was going to have to get coaching from Leslie. Mrs. Myers always caught him when his mind was on vacation, but she never seemed to suspect Leslie of not paying attention. He sneaked a glance up that way. Leslie was totally absorbed in her geography book, or so it would appear to anyone who didn't know.

Terabithia was cold in November. They didn't dare build a fire in the castle, though sometimes they would build one outside and huddle around it. For a while Leslie had been able to keep two sleeping bags in the stronghold, but around the first of December her father noticed their absence, and she had to take them back. Actually, Jess made her take them back. It was not that he was afraid of the Burkes exactly. Leslie's parents were young, with straight white teeth and lots of hair—both of them. Leslie called them Judy and Bill, which bothered Jess more than he wanted it to. It was none of his business what Leslie called her parents. But he just couldn't get used to it.

Both of the Burkes were writers. Mrs. Burke wrote novels and, according to Leslie, was more famous than Mr. Burke, who wrote about politics. It was really something to see the shelf that had their books on it. Mrs. Burke was "Judith Hancock" on the cover, which threw you at first, but then if you looked on the back, there was her picture looking very young and serious. Mr. Burke was going back and forth to Washington to finish a book he was working on with someone else, but he had promised Leslie that after Christmas he would stay home and fix up the house and plant his garden and listen to music and read books out loud and write only in his spare time.

They didn't look like Jess's idea of rich, but even he could tell that the jeans they wore had not come off the counter at Newberry's. There was no TV at the Burkes', but there were mountains of records and a stereo set that looked like something off *Star Trek*. And although their car was small and dusty, it was Italian and looked expensive, too.

They were always nice to Jess when he went over, but then they would suddenly begin talking about French politics or string quartets (which he at first thought was a square box made out of string), or how to save the timber wolves or redwoods or singing whales, and he was scared to open his mouth and show once and for all how dumb he was.

He wasn't comfortable having Leslie at his house either. Joyce Ann would stare, her index finger pulling down her mouth and making her drool. Brenda and Ellie always managed some remark about "*girl* friend." His mother acted stiff and funny just the way she did when she had to go up to school about something. Later she would refer to Leslie's "tacky" clothes. Leslie always wore pants, even to school. Her hair was "shorter than a boy's." Her parents were "hardly more than hippies." May Belle either tried to push in with him and Leslie or sulked at being left out. His father had seen Leslie only a few times and had nodded to show that he had noticed her, but his mother said that she was sure he was fretting that his only son did nothing but play with girls, and they both were worried about what would become of it.

Jess didn't concern himself with what would "become of it." For the first time in his life he got up every morning with something to look forward to. Leslie was more than his friend. She was his other, more exciting self—his way to Terabithia and all the worlds beyond.

Terabithia was their secret, which was a good thing, for how could Jess have ever explained it to an outsider? Just walking down the hill toward the woods made something warm and liquid steal through his body. The closer he came to the dry creek bed and the crab apple tree rope the more he could feel the beating of his heart. He grabbed the end of the rope and swung out toward the other bank with a kind of wild exhilaration and landed gently on his feet, taller and stronger and wiser in that mysterious land.

Leslie's favorite place besides the castle stronghold was the pine forest. There the trees grew so thick at the top that the sunshine was veiled. No low bush or grass could grow in that dim light, so the ground was carpeted with golden needles.

"I used to think this place was haunted," Jess had confessed to Leslie the first afternoon he had revved up his courage to bring her there.

"Oh, but it is," she said. "But you don't have to be scared. It's not haunted with evil things."

"How do you know?"

"You can just feel it. Listen."

At first he heard only the stillness. It was the stillness that had always frightened him before, but this time it was like the moment after Miss Edmunds finished a song, just after the chords hummed down to silence. Leslie was right. They stood there, not moving, not wanting the swish of dry needles beneath their feet to break the spell. Far away from their former world came the cry of geese heading southward.

Leslie took a deep breath. "This is not an ordinary place," she whispered. "Even the rulers of Terabithia come into it only at times of greatest sorrow or of greatest joy. We must strive to keep it sacred. It would not do to disturb the Spirits."

He nodded, and without speaking, they went back to the creek bank where they shared together a solemn meal of crackers and dried fruit.

KATHERINE PATERSON

The middle child of five, Katherine Paterson was born in 1932 in Qing Jiang, Jiangsu, China, where her parents were missionaries. All her early memories are of China, where she lived until forced to leave with her family because of World War II. In the United States, Paterson felt like a stranger in a foreign country. This sense of being an outsider, or a "weird little kid," as she has described herself, drew her into writing.

After college, Paterson taught in Virginia and then in Japan. However, by the time she was thirty, Paterson was writing novels for young adults.

Katherine Paterson says her family knows better than to ask about her work when she is trying to get started. *Bridge to Terabithia* was written after her son's best friend was killed. She found it very hard to begin, but, once the first draft was finished, revising the book was a joy.

If you'd like to find out more about Jess and Leslie and their secret land, Terabithia, look for *Bridge to Terabithia* in your school or local library.

The Secret Among

the Stones

ARDATH MAYHAR

The sun was blisteringly hot. Caro pulled her hat down over her ears as a gritty gust threatened to send it flying away down the steep canyon below her perch.

The climb had been hard and dusty. She was exhausted, and she hated wearing a hat, but sitting on this gritty boulder in the desert sun without one would have been crazy.

She was almost at the top of the mesa[1] now, the steep trail behind her leading down into shadow, for the sun was slanting toward the west already. All around was the vast expanse of broken land, flatlands shimmering with heat-haze, flat-topped mesas rising in the distance, scrub showing its dusty green wherever there was a trace or the hope of water.

1. **mesa** [mā′ sə]: a small flat-topped natural elevation.

The others in her class had gone ahead, led by Miss Burke, who never seemed to be troubled by heat or dust or stones in her shoes. Caro could hear the babble of their voices, but once she had the pebble out of her Nike she hated to move.

There was nothing she wanted to see up there on the tableland. Ruins, as far as she was concerned, were nothing but tumbles of rocks. She had no interest in the ancient people who had cut the stones and set them in place.

She took a sip from her canteen, thinking wryly[2] how silly she'd thought it when Miss Burke insisted that every member of the class must have one, filled, before the bus left the motel.

The shadows beneath the height were inky in contrast to the bone-pale glare of the sun. She gazed into the depths, resting her eyes, and edges and curves came into focus.

That looked like a fascinating place down there, Caro thought. Instead of going up, which was going to be hot and tiring, she decided to go down again and cut back into the shade of the canyon. The last member of the class had already gone by, and nobody could make an objection.

Caro tied her scarf over her hat to help hold it on, made sure that her Nikes were free of pebbles, and started down. Miss Burke was entirely too far away now to notice one of her sheep going astray. The guide was leading the group. By the time anyone realized she was gone, the class would be back down on a level with her destination.

The way down was surprisingly difficult, because it was hard to see the footing. Miss Burke had cautioned everyone about walking carefully, and now Caro saw why. A misstep could send her tumbling down the steep path to splatter on the rocks below.

She felt her way cautiously, watching her feet, freezing when she heard a slithery sound that might be a snake. It turned out to be a dust-colored lizard, but she found her heart thudding hard and hot liquid rising in her throat. What if it *had* been a rattlesnake? She shivered and went even more slowly.

---

2. **wryly** [rī′ lē]: with twisted humor.

At the bottom of the slope the raw-edged cut, which her party had ignored before, led into a walled space opening out into a wider area. The sandy grit of the floor was swept into riffles by the wind pulled through the corridor in the rock; she had a strange feeling that no human being had ever set foot there.

Now that she was out of the sun, Caro's eyes adjusted to the dimness. Someone had been there after all. There were markings on the walls, random doodlings as if someone had occupied him- or herself by drawing circles and jagged lines of lightning and stick figures. She went close and stared up at the pictures, which must have been drawn by someone much taller than she.

There was a story there, she thought, running her gaze along the wall of the canyon. There had been a terrible rain—the slanting dashes couldn't be anything else. Then the sun had cooked everything, for she could see horned shapes that had to be the skulls of buffalo and crosshatched marks that might mean the ground had cracked with drought. There were sketchy shapes of buffalo and deer and men holding sticks and bows.

Interesting. Caro was glad she had stopped and let the others go on without her. She had seen many pictures of the ruins on top of the mesa, but she'd never seen anything about this slot of canyon with drawings on its walls.

She moved back and forth across the space, checking for further markings, but there were no more. Instead, she saw a cave cut back into the eastern wall, its entrance so low that even she would have to stoop and crawl to get inside. A good place for snakes, Caro suspected, but even so she bent to stare into the dark recess.

There was something inside. A bundle of cloth? A stick? Something else, hard to see in the depths where it lay.

Score another for Miss Burke. She had dictated the contents of each hiker's pack, and there had to be a small flashlight and spare batteries. Caro had considered it silly, carrying all this stuff for miles up and down desert heights, but now she had a light.

She thumbed the button, and the narrow beam flicked into the little cave. She gave a stifled shriek and fell back to sit in the grit, staring at the thing that looked back at her from hollow eye sockets. She was almost eye to eye with a skull.

Feeling a chill of terror, Caro shivered, but she didn't retreat. Now she could see that the bundle was clothing of some kind. The stick was a leg bone, which she recognized only because they had studied bones in science last month.

The skull was small, not any larger than her own, she thought. Wisps of black hair straggled from its crown, and it lay on the dusty remnants of a long braid. Even a fragment of a feather still clung to the strands.

Caro had a sudden feeling that this had been a girl, just like herself. Had she been trapped here and starved to death? The entry into the canyon looked raw as if it had recently been cracked open by some shifting of the rock. Could it have been another such shift that caught this one here?

But surely there was another end to the canyon. She scrambled upright and ran to see. The space ended after a dozen winding yards at a wall of rock that went up and up, as smoothly as if it had been sliced with a knife. There wasn't a handhold to be seen. Suddenly sure that she was right—the girl had been trapped—Caro returned to the cave and sat down on a flat stone to stare, fascinated and repelled,[3] at her find.

This was a well-known area in a national park. Surely the archaeologists had known about this place for years and had studied those markings and measured this pitiful remnant of humanity. Yet if that were so, why hadn't they removed it to a museum or something? It didn't make much sense.

The canyon was warmer than she had expected, and Caro took off her hat and fanned herself as she sat in the shadow of the cliff, trying to decide what to do. The skull gazed with mournful intensity into the beam of her flash. The teeth were small, even, not jagged and stained like those of the museum skulls. This had to be a child about her own age, twelve or so.

Caro searched the interior of the space with her light, but she could see no movement that might be a snake. No scorpion sidled

3. **repelled** [ri peld′]: unhappy, disgusted.

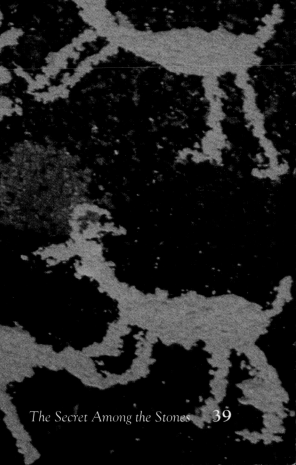

out of range. She felt compelled, though she had no idea why, to venture in and sort out this discovery.

"I am not brave," she said, marveling at the impulse. "I can't stand spiders or blood or anything my brothers like. But I have got to see what's in there. This is *mine*!"

Laying aside her hat, she went down on hands and knees, holding the flash in her teeth. She moved into the cramped space. It was low and dry, and smelled of dust and something very, very old. Not a dead smell, but a snuffy, acrid[4] one.

When she was within a few feet of the pitiful little body, she stopped and looked at it, holding herself still with an effort. Behind the bundle of clothing was another leg bone, bent at the knee. A fall of finger bones extended from beneath a flap of leather sleeve, and something bright— beads?—decorated the upper part of the garment.

Caro knew better than to touch anything, but she felt it couldn't hurt to see it all, now that she had begun. She crawled forward and peered into the shadow

4. **acrid** [ak′ rid]: sharp, bitter.

behind the bundle of clothing. A small shape lay beside the other skeletal hand.

This was easily identified: a doll, made of a stick, with some sort of fur for hair and a leather dress. Two stick legs extended from beneath the dusty skirt.

Caro breathed a long sigh and settled onto the floor of the cave, knowing she had been right. She closed her eyes and saw, as if she were there, a little girl dressed in leather, playing in this shady place with her doll.

The vision seemed true and real, and she clicked off the flashlight, gazing into that distant past. The child was singing softly, a sort of chant, as she rocked the doll in her arms.

"Ai-hi-yee! Ai-hi-yee!" echoed in Caro's mind.

This was a secret place, Caro thought, forgotten by the child's elders, though the markings on the walls showed that others had known it. She came here, as Caro often went to her own secret place beyond the rock formation at home, to think, to dream, to sing to her doll.

As Caro watched that vision, the dream-sky darkened, making the canyon go black as night. Lightning scarred the upper air, its flash brightening the canyon in short bursts. There came a terrific blast of sound, followed by a rumble and a roar.

Terror filled her, and Caro opened her eyes and clicked on the light again. The little shape lay still, its shadow harsh behind it, and Caro knew she had dreamed truly. This child had been trapped here by a rockslide caused, perhaps, by a lightning strike; nobody among her people had known where to search for her.

"Did you starve to death?" She shivered. "Were you even more afraid than I was, just now?" Caro murmured, bending forward to lay a comforting hand on the leather sleeve.

Where she touched it, the ancient material powdered away to dust, leaving the slender arm bones exposed. Caro sighed. No, she mustn't touch anything else. She had to get Miss Burke, even if it meant climbing to the top of the mesa to report this discovery.

She felt sure the most recent storm, with the landslips and

rockslides it had set off a few weeks back, must have opened the way that ancient catastrophe had closed. There had been something on the news about an earth tremor caused by water going down into crevices[5] in the mesas.

She backed out and retrieved her hat. Then Caro hurried to find her teacher, who knew what to do about everything. She met the group coming down the mesa, calling her name anxiously and searching every crevice into which she might have fallen.

"Oh, Miss Burke! I'm not lost, just out of pocket. I've found something awful and wonderful!" she panted.

"Carolyn, I cannot have my charges running off in country like this! It's dangerous. . . . *What* have you found?" Miss Burke was an amateur archaeologist,[6] and any hint of ancient finds caught her attention instantly.

By the time she saw the newly opened way into the canyon and the small bones in the cave, Miss Burke was as excited as she ever allowed herself to become. "I will inform the Rangers as soon as we get back to the motel," she said, her gaze fixed longingly on the half-visible bundle beneath the cliff.

She turned to José, who had been the guide for this field trip. "It will surprise me if this is not extremely unusual. Not because of the skeleton, of course, but because of the petroglyphs."[7]

He stared into the cave, still looking astonished. "I think maybe you are right," he said. "We will call the University when we have the chance."

Caro felt sure this was something really important. She had a vision of returning in triumph to the scene of her discovery. The Carolyn Wheaton Canyon Area had a nice ring to it. She had a sudden vision of her triumph, lights, reporters, awed schoolmates and teachers.

5. **crevices** [krev′ is əz]: narrow splits or cracks.
6. **archaeologist** [är′ kē ol′ ə jist]: someone who studies bones and ancient places to learn about the people, customs, and life of the past.
7. **petroglyphs** [pe′ trə glifz′]: drawings or carvings on rock, made by prehistoric people.

Then she thought of that dark cave where the small skeleton still lay, heard again in her memory the devastating thunder, felt again the cold despair that had touched her as she crouched in that place.

There was tragedy here, not triumph. The fame that might come of it was not hers at all.

"Ai-hi-yee!" she whispered, as she bent to look through the dimness into those empty eyes once more. "Ai-hi-yee!"

The small, even teeth grinned at her silently.

Caro smiled back. She had done her best for this lost one. Maybe—who could say?—this girl knew at last that she was no longer alone.

ARDATH MAYHAR

Ardath Mayhar was born in 1930 in Timpson, Texas, and raised on her family's dairy farm. Mayhar was, as she says, "a very strange, small child" who grew into a teenager with her own way of looking at the world while "shoveling manure, writing poetry, and looking up at the stars." After leaving home, Mayhar worked in a bookstore where she met her future husband. Following several years in Oregon, the Mayhars moved back to Texas, to their home in a wild spot where they could hear wolves and see bobcat, bear, and cougar. "It is ideal for writing the sort of fantasy I do best," Mayhar says.

Mayhar writes every day. "On days when fiction lies there like a wart on a frog, I write letters," she says. When she needs a change, she goes to science fiction conventions.

"The Secret Among the Stones" came out of research Mayhar did for a novel, *The People of the Mesa*. Always interested in the Anasazi people, Mayhar says, "The deeper I dug, the greater my fascination became. This small story used only one tiny fragment."

The Cave

GLENN W. DRESBACH

Sometimes when the boy was troubled he would go
    To a little cave of stone above the brook
And build a fire just big enough to glow
    Upon the ledge outside, then sit and look.
Below him was the winding silver trail   5
    Of water from the upland pasture springs,
And meadows where he heard the calling quail;
    Before him was the sky, and passing wings.

The tang[1] of willow twigs he lighted there,
    Fragrance of meadows breathing slow and deep,   10
The cave's own musky[2] coolness on the air,
    The scent of sunlight . . . all were his to keep.
We had such places—cave or tree or hill . . .
    And we are lucky if we keep them still.

1. **tang** [tang]: a strong flavor or odor.
2. **musky** [mus′ kē]: a strong, sharp odor.

GLENN W. DRESBACH

Glenn W. Dresbach [1889-1968] was born in Lanark, Illinois, and grew up loving the outdoors. He especially loved hunting and fishing. Dresbach's first job, as an accountant, took him to the Panama Canal Zone, where the jungle provided opportunities for exploration. Once back in the United States, he held several other jobs. Meanwhile, he wrote poetry—lots of poetry. In his later years, Dresbach was crippled in an accident and confined to his home in the Ozark Mountains. Even though he had to give up his favorite outdoor activities, Dresbach led an active life, keeping in touch with the world of poetry as long as he lived.

The CAVE

ENRIQUE JARAMILLO LEVI

A white dog with dark spots was sniffing around a fire hydrant in front of the store window. On the other side of the window, the shapes of objects looked blurred. I opened the door to my father's store and a little bell rang. When I was about to enter, I had the distinct impression that a large, cavernous[1] mouth was going to swallow me. I went inside anyway.

I was welcomed by my cat. My sweet cat. His sad, crossed eyes looked at me tamely as he arched his back. Yellow, blue, and white neon lights flickered on and off. The walls had the familiar scents of incense[2] and pine. I hesitated[3] for a moment. I looked behind the

1. **cavernous** [kav′ ər nəs]: large and hollow.
2. **incense** [in′ sens]: a substance that gives off a sweet odor when burned.
3. **hesitated** [həz′ ə tāt əd]: held back, stopped.

counter and saw that my father was busy helping a client who looked Chinese. I continued walking toward that place I had been told many times not to enter.

After walking down the long hallway lined with old chests and forgotten furniture, I entered "the cave." That was what my older brother called it. He would tell me, "Dad stores all kinds of strange things in there. Every time I go inside, it seems that the stuffed crocodiles look at me as if they're unhappy. I wonder why those crocodiles are in the cellar. They're probably just iguanas[4] or gigantic lizards Dad's collected."

All kinds of old clothing that looked like theater costumes hung on hooks randomly[5] nailed into the walls of the cellar. I touched the silk, worn and dirty, and a horrible spider almost bit me. I screamed once and just then the little white wooden horse with the broken leg, which had disappeared mysteriously a long time ago, rocked forward, greeting me happily from his corner covered with cobwebs. The mild breeze that filtered[6] through the airshaft[7] gently swayed a piece of salted codfish that hung from the ceiling on a wire. I don't know what made me stretch out my hand at that moment and pull off a piece of that dark, leathery skin and chew on it, tasting the salt that reminded me of seas sailed by pirates.

I continued walking into the darkness. I sensed shadows moving in the back of the room and heard small, squeaky sounds. I started fighting the fear I was feeling and my heart started pounding like crazy. I felt strange sensations on my skin and I didn't know if it was just my imagination or if they were caused by spirits I couldn't see. I stopped to listen. Yes, now it was loud. I heard a screech. I lifted my foot; it became completely silent in the cave.

4. **iguanas** [i gwä′ nəz]: large tropical American lizards with spiny crests.
5. **randomly** [ran′ dəm lē]: by chance, without a definite plan or purpose.
6. **filtered** [fil′ tərd]: passed, as if through a strainer.
7. **airshaft** [ār′ shaft]: passage that allows fresh air to circulate.

Twisted wires hanging out of boxes created strange shapes. Foul smells seeped[8] from ancient bottles and made me feel dizzy. I suddenly saw the beady eyes of a huge rat. I screamed and saw them fade in the darkness. I felt strange things bumping into my ankles, and I took a step back. And another. I tripped on some rolled-up wire that I thought was a rattlesnake coiling around my feet. I wanted to run, but I tripped and fell into a box that was inside another larger box. I felt very small. And in fact I was, because I saw the enormous eyes of my cat shining like streetlights in the darkness. They stared at me for a long time, hypnotically,[9] as if everything had suddenly stopped forever. The cat stretched out his big front paws and placed them on the edge of the larger box, breaking that strange trance we were in.

8. **seeped** [sēpd]: leaked slowly.
9. **hypnotically** [hip not′ ik lē]: as if in a daze.

As he was stretching, he lowered that gigantic, threatening head. I saw myself reflected in those liquid pools that continued staring at me. "It's me . . . Anita!" I said, trying to calm him down. But he opened his mouth wide. I was disgusted by the smell of codfish on his breath.

I saw the sharp points of his fangs coming closer. I could see them slowly penetrating[10] the darkness. In one swift movement, I managed to grab onto one of the long, elastic hairs of his whiskers and swing on it with the hope of being able to jump out of the box. I closed my eyes so I wouldn't tremble before those bewildered[11] crossed eyes that were right in front of me, that continued watching me sway from side to side.

10. **penetrating** [pen′ ə trāt ing]: entering into, filling.
11. **bewildered** [bi wil′ dərd]: confused, puzzled.

I let go of his whisker and fell on the rolled-up wire, which wrapped itself around me. I couldn't move. I was a tiny doll trapped in a whirlpool of metallic waves that vibrated like shiny, new springs. A loud meow made me look up. His wide, dark mouth with sharp fangs was getting closer.

Suddenly a light was turned on. The cat ran away. My father's strong hands started to unravel[12] the wires that had me trapped. I looked up at his face for some kind of an explanation, a signal. I saw only his usual expression, as if nothing out of the ordinary had happened. He helped me stand up and I brushed off the dust trying to get rid of the bad memories. Everything went back to normal. I confirmed[13] this when the mirror on the wall reflected my normal height. But my bones ached. They felt strange, taut,[14] and hot inside. A little bell rang. I knew a new customer was coming in. Dad left and made a gesture with his hand for me to follow him. Before leaving, I wanted to look at myself in the mirror one more time. I saw the cat approach me from behind. As usual, I was at least three times as big as he. Then the cat meowed. I turned around to face him. His crossed eyes shone under the light that hung from the ceiling. "You're not a bad kitten . . . are you?" I whispered. I felt the heat tingling in my bones. As my cat walked away, swaying his impertinent[15] tail, I'm sure I saw him wink at me.

For weeks after, I felt a lot of pain in my bones when it rained, especially at night. I never again went near cats. My brother thinks that I fell asleep in the cave that day and had a bad nightmare. Of course that is the most logical[16] explanation. Anybody would say that.

But only I know that even today, so many years later, when it rains a lot and it's cold, I still get under the covers, afraid to look at myself in the mirror.

12. **unravel** [un rav′ əl]: separate, pull apart.
13. **confirmed** [kən fėrmd′]: proved to be true.
14. **taut** [tôt]: tight, tense.
15. **impertinent** [im pėrt′ n ənt]: rudely bold.
16. **logical** [loj′ ə kəl]: reasonable, sensible.

E N R I Q U E
J A R A M I L L O
L E V I

....

Enrique Jaramillo Levi was born in
Colón, Panama. He now is a professor
of Latin American literature. He has
written and published collections of
poetry and short stories, the most
well-known being *Duplicaciones*
(Duplications) (1989).

A
Brother's
Promise

PAM CONRAD

I

Annie watched Geoffrey's every move. Her brother looked very different since he had gone away to art school in Paris. He was almost a stranger, with his new mustache and fancy clothes. She watched him butter his bread while he spoke to their parents, and she imitated the way he smoothed the butter and folded his slice of bread in half.

Her father was speaking in a loud booming voice. "The *Times*[1] said last week that this Statue of Liberty gift may be a hoax played on the American people by the French. They say it's possible the statue doesn't even exist."

"But Father," Geoffrey objected, "I've seen it with my own eyes." Annie watched his cheeks flush with excitement. "It towers over the houses on a small Parisian street. It's wonderful! The reason it hasn't arrived here yet has nothing to do with the French people. The problem is with the American people, who haven't collected any money for a pedestal."

"You mean," said Annie, "that when we build the pedestal, they will send over the whole statue?"

"And not until then," Geoffrey answered.

"How long have the statue's hand and torch been here in Madison Square?"[2] she asked. She thought of it rising over the trees just a few blocks away. It had been there nearly all her life, and she was used to it. Until now, until there was talk of sending it back to Paris because there was no pedestal.

"Let's see," her father said, stroking his thick mustache and gazing into the chandelier.[3] "The hand and the torch came over in 1876 for

1. **Times** [tīmz]: the *New York Times*, a daily newspaper.
2. **Madison Square** [mad´ ə sən skwār]: a section of New York City.
3. **chandelier** [shan´ də lir´]: a branched light fixture, usually hanging from the ceiling.

the United States Centennial Exposition[4] in Philadelphia—where, I might add, its presence did little to encourage donations for a pedestal—and in 1877 it was brought here to New York. How old was Annie, dear?" he asked, turning to his wife.

She was pouring Geoffrey more coffee, holding her heavy lace sleeves away from the urn. "Annie was about five, I believe, and now she's twelve, so the statue must have been here for seven years."

"Are you really twelve already, Annie?" Geoffrey asked, suddenly noticing her and smiling across the table. It was that smile that made him so familiar again.

"You missed my birthday as usual, Geoffrey," she teased. "Otherwise you'd know how old I am. Besides, I'm ten years younger than you are, so you should never forget."

"Oh, but I forget how old *I* am," he said, teasing her.

Annie rolled her eyes. "Well, have you forgotten the way to Madison Square?"

"Probably," he replied.

They grinned at each other. Annie was glad he was home, even for just a visit. Now she wanted to go to the Square and up into the torch with him. "Would you like me to lead you there?" she asked.

"Sounds wonderful!" Geoffrey folded his napkin and put it next to his plate. "If you'll excuse us, Mother, Father, we're off to the statue."

"For one last look," Annie added, "before the hand is returned forever to Paris just because the stingy Americans won't make a pedestal for her."

"Don't say that, Annie," Geoffrey objected, pushing his chair quietly under the table. "Nothing is forever."

Geoffrey walked around the table and offered her his arm. "Well, let's go see her, shall we, mademoiselle?[5] Get your wrap, and we're off."

4. **Exposition** [eks′ spə zish′ ən]: a public show, similar to a world's fair.
5. **mademoiselle** [mäd mwä zel′]: miss, an unmarried woman.

II

It was a cold blustery morning as Annie and Geoffrey ran down the polished front stoop of their home and started toward Madison Square. Annie kept her cold hands tucked deep inside her furry muff, and she grew sadder and sadder as they walked along.

"What if Father is right, Geoffrey? What if the hand goes back to Paris? We'll never see it again."

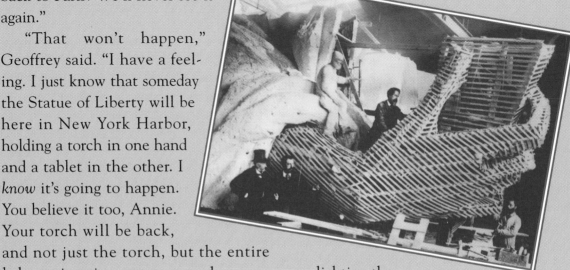

"That won't happen," Geoffrey said. "I have a feeling. I just know that someday the Statue of Liberty will be here in New York Harbor, holding a torch in one hand and a tablet in the other. I *know* it's going to happen. You believe it too, Annie. Your torch will be back, and not just the torch, but the entire lady, as gigantic a statue as you have ever seen, lighting the harbor and welcoming ships and people from all over the world."

They walked quickly in the winter wind, until they could see the torch and the hand in the middle of the Square. It was a sight Annie had seen nearly every day for the last seven years, but when she saw it with Geoffrey it was always better.

"Look at that, Annie. Can you imagine the size she will be? A nose as tall as you are? Eyes this big?" He motioned with his hands. "What a wonderful day it will be when she's finally in the harbor!"

Annie smiled. "Can you remember the first time we went up inside the torch, Geoffrey? Do you remember?"

"Of course. Mother was furious at me for taking you up." He shook his head. "I can still see her horrified face as her little Annie stood on the railing—held tightly by me, I might add—waving her doll and calling, 'Momma! Momma!'" He tossed back his head and laughed. "You were so funny!"

"Do you know that's the first memory I have in my whole life?" she said. "It's the very first thing I remember—being up in that torch with you holding on to me, and seeing Mother and Father like little people on the ground below us."

"I'm glad," Geoffrey said softly. "That's a wonderful first memory."

Annie felt tears burn her eyes. "Oh, but it's not fair! I don't want it to go back to Paris! I don't want to lose it. We've had so much fun here. What if it never comes back?"

"Nonsense!" said Geoffrey, as they approached the stone base of the statue that loomed three stories above them. They entered the base and started up the narrow staircase that was lit by gas lamps. At the top, they stepped onto a railed, circular walkway. Geoffrey pulled his silver spyglass out of his vest pocket and let her peer through it up and down Fifth Avenue and Broadway. The wind was howling through the metalwork, and the noise of the horse and carriage traffic filtered through the park's lining of bare trees.

They shared the spyglass between them, as they had so many times in the past, each quiet in thought. Annie was sure that this was the last time she would stand like this in the great torch overlooking her city. She had an awful feeling that something terrible was going to happen. Something terrible that she couldn't stop. She sighed and leaned on the railing.

"Oh, now, now," Geoffrey said, patting her shoulder. "No sadness today. Try not to think of this as the end, but as the beginning.

"The beginning?" asked Annie.

"The beginning of what this all was originally intended to be, a beautiful statue in the harbor."

"It will never happen," she said.

"Let's make a pact," he said. "I, Geoffrey Gibbon, swear that I will return to this torch someday with you. I promise that one day we'll stand in this very spot, only it will be higher, much higher, nearly a hundred and fifty feet in the sky, overlooking the harbor and all of the city and country of New York, and *that* will be a great day."

"Describe it to me, Geoffrey," she said quietly.

"We'll stand in this very spot," he began, "and when we look over the edge, we'll look down into the statue's huge face. We'll stand right here and see our country spread out before us—the seas, the hills, the people everywhere celebrating and happy."

Annie smiled and looked at him, glad he was home. "You say things so nicely, Geoffrey."

"Now, *you* promise," he said.

Annie straightened up and squared her shoulders. "I, Annie Gibbon, promise to come back to this very spot, wherever this spot may be, whenever that may be, with you, Geoffrey. And it will be a great day."

They smiled at each other, and Annie felt all her worries lift from her shoulders, like birds flying away. Then some people came up onto the walkway beside them.

"Do you believe this monstrosity?" one of them said. "Have you ever seen such a ridiculous lighthouse?"

Annie and Geoffrey looked at each other. He winked, and his mustache twitched ever so slightly.

III

It was almost a year since Geoffrey had returned to Paris and the American papers were brimming with news of a campaign to bring the statue to America at last. Happily, Annie let the wind sweep her across the cobblestone street, weaving her in and out of the slow-moving carriages, and then let it push her up the polished stone steps of her home. Her one hand was jammed into her fur muff, and the other clutched a copy of the day's *New York World*.[6]

The heavy door opened easily, and as she unwound her scarf from around her neck, she began calling, "Mother! Father!" Annie stomped into the parlor, flashing the newspaper at her parents, who sat unusually still on the velvet lounge by the fireplace. "It's really coming! We're really going to get the whole statue, and Geoffrey and I will go up into the torch again, just like he promised, only this time it will be in the harbor, not in the park.

"Imagine!" she cried. "No one thought Americans could raise the money to build the pedestal, but according to the *New York World*, pennies and nickels are pouring in from all over."

"Annie," her mother said softly.

Annie rustled the day's newspaper in front of her. "They have a goal of one hundred thousand dollars to raise, and they just might be able to do it."

"Annie," her mother repeated.

"I'm so excited," Annie continued. "I'm going to earn some money and make my contribution. Have you any idea what this means? Geoffrey was right after all.

"Oh, I must write to Geoffrey! He will be so excited! He knew it! He knew it all along!" She looked from her mother to her father for the first time, and then she saw that her mother had been crying and her father was pale.

6. **New York World**: a New York newspaper, purchased by Joseph Pulitzer in 1883, that favored the Democratic party.

"Please, Annie," her mother said, her voice shaky and uncertain.

"What is it, Mother?" she asked. "What's wrong?"

"It's Geoffrey, dear," her mother whispered. "Your brother is dead." Annie's mother dropped her head into her hands and began to cry.

"What are you talking about? What do you mean?"

Her father's voice was choked and soft. "He's been killed in an accident, Annie. I can't believe it."

Annie felt frozen to the ground. Her ears were ringing. Her arms grew numb. "What happened?"

"It seems he was visiting with some people in Germany, riding in some kind of motorized vehicle. It went out of control. He was killed instantly."

"How do you know this?" Annie shouted, not wanting to believe she'd never see her brother again.

Her father pointed to the parlor table in front of him, to a letter beside a box. It was posted in Germany, and like all Geoffrey's letters, it had unusual and colorful stamps, but the handwriting was unfamiliar.

Annie read over the letter—the accident, the death—to the closing. "I extend my deepest sympathy. I'm sending a package to Annie, whom Geoffrey spoke of with deepest affection. It's one of his possessions that I feel he would have wanted her to have. Sincerely, Walter Linderbaum."

Annie reached out and touched the brown box beside the letter. She lifted it and gently unwrapped the paper. It was a wooden box. She pried it open and inside, nestled in cork, was Geoffrey's spyglass. Dear Geoffrey's rare and beautiful spyglass, etched in silver, trimmed in polished wood. She could almost feel the wind howling through the railings of the statue's hand, almost hear the noise of the horse and carriage traffic filtering through the trees. She held the spyglass up to her eye and looked out the window through the fine lace curtains. She looked and looked and looked until she could no longer see past her tears.

IV

In a few weeks, Annie wrote this letter to the publisher of the *New York World* newspaper:

Dear Mr. Pulitzer,

> *I am sending this money for the Statue of Liberty Pedestal Fund. I live near Madison Square, and I used to visit the torch with my older brother, Geoffrey. Geoffrey was an art student in Paris, and he told me all about the statue and how the man who built the Eiffel Tower in Paris also built the foundation of the Statue of Liberty. He told me how the statue towers over the buildings in Paris, and how he used to look at it and imagine it in New York Harbor. We even made a solemn promise to meet in the torch when it was finally here again. He was always so certain that she would be here one day.*
>
> *I want to make sure of it. You see, my brother died this year, and although he can't keep his promise to me, I can still keep mine; I've been to see a local pawnbroker, and I sold Geoffrey's rare antique spyglass made of silver and wood that we used to look around New York City, from up inside the torch. I'm sad to sell it, but I'm sure he'd understand. Please take this money in Geoffrey Gibbon's memory. And please build a pedestal.*

Respectfully yours,
Annie Gibbon

Annie's letter was published in the *New York World*, and its heartfelt message touched off a series of contributions in memory of beloved relatives. Annie was proud to see the fund grow bigger every week until, finally, Joseph Pulitzer declared the fund to be complete, and the construction of the pedestal on Bedloe's Island[7] was to begin at last.

---

7. **Bedloe's Island** [bed′ lōz]: the former name of Liberty Island, where the Statue of Liberty is located.

V

October 28, 1886, was a cold, drizzly day, but it was declared a holiday, and New York was astir with excitement. Even though the city was in a festive mood, Annie felt uneasy. Her parents had promised to take her to Bedloe's Island to see the statue that had finally arrived and had been assembled on its glorious pedestal, but Annie wasn't sure she wanted to see it. It wouldn't be the same without Geoffrey. If he couldn't see it, maybe she shouldn't see it either, she thought. But she got into the carriage with her mother and father and headed to the pier, where they would take a boat over to the island.

Annie was quiet in the carriage as she watched the holiday crowds out the window. Her mother patted her hand reassuringly. "I guess we all miss Geoffrey this day," her mother said. "He would have enjoyed this."

"Oh, yes," sighed Annie, watching the American and French flags on the fronts of buildings. "This should be Geoffrey's day. He saw the statue in Paris, and he should be here today."

They were all quiet and sad and rode in silence until they reached the pier. Her father found the people who would take them across. Annie boarded a boat with her parents, and they started out toward Bedloe's Island. The harbor was afloat with every kind of boat—from ferryboats and freighters to yachts, scows, and battleships. The steam from all the steamships put a cloud over

The Unveiling of the Statue of Liberty Enlightening the World Edward Moran, 1886, oil on canvas, 49 ½″ x 39 ½″, Museum of the City of New York

the harbor, but everywhere there was music—"Yankee Doodle Dandy," the "Marseillaise"[8]—and the laughter of people celebrating.

Annie stood shivering by the railing of the boat. Looming ahead, standing majestically in the center of the harbor, was the

8. **Marseillaise** [mär sā yez′]: the French national anthem.

shape of a gigantic lady holding a torch in one hand and a tablet in the other.

"You believe it too, Annie," she could almost hear Geoffrey say. "The Statue of Liberty will be here in New York Harbor—the entire lady, lighting the harbor and welcoming ships and people from all over the world." Tears filled Annie's eyes. She was suddenly glad she had come.

"Look," she whispered. "Look at her, Geoffrey."

Annie had never seen so much excitement and merriment in her life. President Grover Cleveland was there, with bands and dignitaries, and there were speeches and songs and cheers and patriotic excitement. She and her parents joined the crowds and listened to the speeches. She was especially excited when Joseph Pulitzer took the stand and gave his speech. He talked about the American people who had finally come through. He talked about the great crews that had built the pedestal, the wonderful French people who had sent the statue to us. He called it the greatest gift one nation ever gave another. The crowds cheered and laughed, and Joseph Pulitzer beamed with pride as if he had brought the statue over single-handedly.

Then, just when it seemed he was through, he looked over the crowd thoughtfully and shouted out, "By the way, is Annie Gibbon here today?"

"What?" her mother gasped.

Annie froze in disbelief.

"Annie Gibbon?" Joseph Pulitzer called once again.

"Here I am!" Annie cried, waving from her place in the crowd.

"Come up here, Annie!" He laughed, and the crowd parted for her. She made her way to the podium, barely knowing what she was doing, barely believing this was really happening. Mr. Pulitzer reached out his hand and guided her up the steps. He kept her at his side and spoke to the crowd.

"I don't know if you folks remember, but Annie wrote a letter to me that we published in the *World* a while ago. Isn't that right, Annie?" he said, turning to her and smiling.

She nodded numbly.

"Well, I'm so glad you're here. You see," he said, turning back to his audience, "she lost her brother last year, a brother who loved the Statue of Liberty. He'd actually seen it in Paris, and Annie sold his special spyglass and sent the money to the Pedestal Fund in his memory. And that led many others to do the same thing."

A few people clapped, and Annie looked down at their faces.

"Annie, I have a surprise for you." He turned around, and someone handed him a long, thin wooden box. "When I read your letter, I sent my people out to all the pawnshops in your area. I said to myself, 'Joseph, when the statue comes over, that little girl is going to have her spyglass back. Yes, she is.' Now you take this spyglass and climb to the top of that lady and take a good look around, Annie."

People were laughing and clapping, and Joseph Pulitzer was nearly bursting with himself. But all Annie could see was the familiar box in her hand. Carefully she opened it, not believing, but, yes, Geoffrey's spyglass was nestled in the box, waiting for her. The band began to play, and Annie looked up into the face of Joseph Pulitzer. "Thank you," she whispered.

VI

Annie's parents walked her to the base of the statue, where they hugged her and let her go up alone. Holding the spyglass box tightly in her hand, she started up the stairway. The inside of the statue was immense, studded with bolts and held together with girders and supports. She remembered how once Geoffrey had carried her up the stairs in the torch. How huge the torch had seemed then, but it was nothing like this! She climbed and climbed and climbed, 161 steps, never stopping at a rest station, and not even stopping at the observation room in the crown.

Then Annie entered the part of the statue that was so familiar to her. She began to climb up into the raised arm. Her hand touched the cold metal wall; her feet sounded lightly on the stairs. She was alone. Up and up, until at last she stepped out onto the circular walkway around the base of the torch. She felt as if she had arrived home, but only for an instant, and then her breath was whisked away. She had known she would not see Fifth Avenue and Broadway, but there was no way she could have prepared herself for what was before her. She was certain if she reached up she could have touched the gray clouds, yet she clasped the railing tightly with her gloved fingers. The wind whipped around her, whistling through the gratings, and the earth stretched out in all directions.

"Describe it to me, dear Annie," she thought she heard a voice say.

Her words were blown away by the wind, but she began slowly. "When I look over the edge, I can see down into the statue's beautiful face. Her nose is strong and straight, and I can see her lips, proud and determined. The spikes of her crown are huge and studded with bolts. In her hand is a tablet that reads, 'July 4, 1776.' I am standing in the torch that symbolizes the light of freedom, and before me I can see my country spread wide and far, the seas, the hills, and the people everywhere celebrating and happy. I can hear the band, and I can see battleships and steamships, and in the distance I see buildings and steeples. On the ground, I can see people like tiny ants."

She smiled, raised her spyglass to her eye, and scanned the crowds below. "I can't even find Mother and Father." Then she turned the spyglass to the horizon. "It's the haziest of days; Geoffrey. It's difficult to see. I'll have to come back again one day." She smiled. "Yes, I'll come back on a clear day, when I can see the hills and the distant horizon. There will be more days, many more, and I'll come back again and again. I promise. You were right, Geoffrey. This is a great day."

Annie stayed as long as she could, until the wind and the cold seemed to be buffeting her from every direction, and then she started down. On her way home, skimming across the harbor in the boat, Annie turned back to the statue and watched her there in the twilight. A few fireworks had gone up in the foggy night, and everywhere boats were lit with bright lights and lanterns.

And then slowly, very slowly, the torch in the great lady's hand began to glow. It was dim at first, and then brighter, until it glowed with a fierce and proud light. Annie watched, and she was certain that from across the dark waters of the harbor the torch light faintly, but surely, winked at her.

PAM CONRAD

Pam Conrad was born in 1947 in New York City. She began to write when she was seven and was at home with chickenpox. "My mother gave me paper, thinking I would draw," she says, "but I began writing poetry. From then on, whenever I got a fever, I would write poetry." Luckily Conrad also learned to write when she was healthy.

Although she has produced many different types of writing, Conrad especially loves to write stories. She has always been fascinated with history. Her novel *Prairie Songs* comes out of her feeling for the difficulties of pioneer life. Most of all, she "likes the idea of looking into the past to imagine what it would have been like to live then."

The story "A Brother's Promise" was inspired, Conrad says, by a novel she read in which the main character is carried back in time and goes up into the hand of the Liberty statue as it stood in Madison Square Park.

Another historical novel, *Pedro's Journal,* tells the story of a ship's boy as he sailed with Christopher Columbus on the Santa Maria.

THE LIGHTWELL

LAURENCE YEP

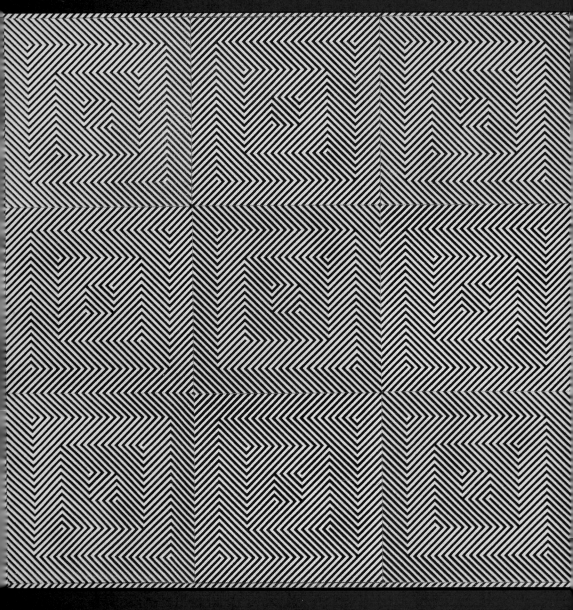

My grandmother lives in a tiny studio apartment in Chinatown. Her home, in the rear of the building, receives no direct sunlight even though her window opens on a lightwell;[1] for the lightwell seems to stretch endlessly upward and downward among the many buildings. At its brightest, it is filled with a kind of tired twilight.

Although the lightwell is a poor source for light, it is a perfect carrier for sound. In the mornings it carries sound from all the other apartments—the slap of wet laundry being hung in a window, the rush of water into a sink, the crying of a baby. During the afternoons, bits of conversation float into my grandmother's home like fragments of little dramas and comedies—just as, I'm sure, the other tenants can hear the shuffling of my grandmother's cards and her exclamations when she loses at solitaire.[2]

Toward evening, as my grandmother clanks pots on her stove, I can hear matching sounds from the other apartments as her neighbors also prepare their meals. And the smell of my grandmother's simmering rice and frying vegetables mingles with the other smells in the lightwell until there are enough aromas for a banquet.

Side by side, top and below, each of us lives in our own separate time and space. And yet we all belong to the same building, our lives touching however briefly and faintly.

1. **lightwell** [līt′ wel]: an interior shaft or opening extending from the bottom to the top of a building, designed to admit light to interior rooms.
2. **solitaire** [sol′ ə tār]: a card game played by one person.

L A U R E N C E   Y E P

Laurence Yep was born in 1948 in San Francisco, California, and grew up as the only Chinese American in an African American neighborhood. Yep went to school in Chinatown, but often felt like an outsider there, too, because he did not speak Chinese. Being an outsider is a theme in many of Yep's stories.

When Yep became interested in the first Chinese immigrants to the United States, he had a lot of research to do because little had been written about their history. Yep's own experiences add to his work. The main character in *Child of the Owl* has a grandmother in Chinatown very much like Yep's own grandmother described in "The Lightwell."

GRANDMAMA'S KITCHEN TABLE

CYNTHIA RYLANT

Since I was four years old I have been talking about my life to the people who sit at my grandmama's kitchen table in Cool Ridge, West Virginia.

The kitchen is small and skinny. There is a little window next to Grandmama's table, and this is where she sits when she is alone in the house. Out it she can see the birds at the apple tree, eating the seed she left them, and she can see who's driving up the hollow, or whose child is walking out the dirt road to the school bus. There are woods all around, and her eyes will follow them down past the creek, down past Bill Mills' house, and on.

When I am visiting, I make sure I never sit in Grandmama's chair. I want her to have her little window.

Relatives will come by—Uncle Dean and Aunt Linda, Sue and the girls, Bev and the baby—and all sit around Grandmama's sturdy old table, even though someone will have to sit on a bench in the doorway or on an extra chair that will block anybody who's trying to get through the room. But no one wants to go into the living room, where there's plenty of seats for us all. We want to be in Grandmama's kitchen, near this heavy old table, and we want to drink coffee and tea and Coke and eat angel food cake or leftover biscuits and talk and talk and talk and talk until we are all talked out, and there is nothing left to do but go on home and rest up and come back tomorrow to talk some more.

CYNTHIA RYLANT

Cynthia Rylant was born in 1954 in Hopewell, Virginia. Between the ages of four and eight, Rylant lived in the West Virginia mountains with her grandmother and grandfather. "They lived life with strength," Rylant says, and with "great calm, a real sense of what it means to be devoted to and responsible for other people." Rylant wanted her writing to reflect the way her grandparents spoke and felt. "Grandmama's Kitchen Table" shows how well she has succeeded.

The rest of Rylant's growing-up years were spent with her mother in a small town called Beaver—a town with no bookstore and no library. In college she read everything, discovering children's literature that she had never known existed. "I loved everything I read," she says. At that point she knew she wanted to write. Rylant has written many books for younger children and others for young adults. *A Fine White Dust* is one of her novels; its narrator is a fourteen-year-old boy.

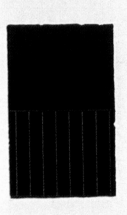

ELEVATOR

LUCILLE CLIFTON

down
in the corner
my book and i
traveling
over the project[1]   5
walls
so the world
is more than this
elevator
stuck between   10
floors again
and home
is a corner
where i crouch
safe   15
reading waiting
to start moving
up

1. **project** [proj′ ekt]: a group of apartment houses
   built as a unit for public housing.

LUCILLE CLIFTON

Lucille Clifton was born in 1936 in Depew, New York. Her father could read but could write only his name. Her mother found time to write poetry. Both parents passed on their belief that there is power in the written word. At sixteen, Clifton received a scholarship to Howard University, in Washington, D.C. When she left Howard after just two years, her parents were shocked, for she was the first in her family to attend college. It was the wrong place for her, Clifton told them, but she knew what she wanted to do. She would write poems.

Clifton began writing. She also went back to college. After graduating in 1955, raising six children took all her time. Clifton did not publish her first book of poems, *Good Times*, for fifteen years. However, when she finally did, she was a success. Clifton has received many awards for her writing. In 1979 she was named Poet Laureate of the State of Maryland. In addition to her poems, Clifton has written her autobiography and stories for children. Much of her work is about African American families in the city. Like "Elevator," most of her poems are for people of any age.

Hunt Farm Maxfield Parrish, 1948, oil on composition board, 23" X 18$^7/_8$",
Hood Museum of Art, Dartmouth College, Hanover, N.H.

Go Home

JANET REED McFATTER

to the fence posts leaning,
the drive pocked.
See the barns stained brown, tobacco red,
their slatted sides tattooed:
Big Chief, Happy Jim.   5

Drive down the pale macadam[1] road;
pass the Burcold farm
where all the blue-eyed Burcolds live
displaying kinship like a deck of cards.

Wave to the barley.   10
Wave to the white cows spotted
dark under the willows.

Listen, listen to the thin tar patches
bump under the tires:
welcome home; welcome home.   15

1. **macadam** [mə kadʹ əm]: road material made of small, broken stones that
   are rolled until solid and smooth.

A Boy and a MOUNTAIN

FROM

Banner in the *Sky*

JAMES RAMSEY ULLMAN

In the heart of the Swiss Alps, on the high frontier between earth and sky, stands one of the great mountains of the world. To men generally it is known as the Citadel, but the people of the valley beneath it seldom call it by that name. They call it the Rudisberg— Rudi's Mountain. And that is because, in the long-gone year of 1865, there lived in that valley a boy called Rudi Matt….

Most of the boys of the village were tall, broad and strongly built. Rudi was small and slim. But to make up for it, he was quick. In all his sixteen years he had probably never been quicker than on a certain summer morning when he slipped out the kitchen door of the Beau Site Hotel and into the alley beyond. When Teo Zurbriggen,[1] the cook, turned from his stove to get a jar from the spice shelf, Rudi had been at his usual place, washing the breakfast dishes. But when, five seconds later, Old Teo turned back, his young helper was gone.

The cook muttered under his breath. But, almost at the same time, he smiled. He smiled because he knew what the boy was up to, and in his old heart he was glad.

1. **Teo Zurbriggen** [tä′ ō tsür′ brē gen]

Outside, Rudi did not follow the alley to the main street. He went in the other direction, came to a second alley, and ran quickly through the back part of the town. He made a wide detour around his mother's house; another around the house of his uncle, Franz Lerner. Fortunately he met no one who knew him—or at least who knew he was supposed to be working in the kitchen of the Beau Site.

Soon he came to the edge of the town and a roaring brook. Across the brook lay a footbridge; but, instead of using it, he worked his way upstream around a bend and then crossed over, leaping agilely[2] from boulder to boulder. From the far side he looked back. Apparently no one had seen him. Scrambling up the bank, he plunged through a clump of bushes, skirted[3] a barnyard and picked up a path through the meadows. Here, for the first time, he stopped running. There was no living thing to be seen except a herd of grazing cows. The only sound was the tinkling of their bells.

2. **agilely** [aj′ əl ē]: moving with speed and grace.
3. **skirted** [skėrt′ əd]: passed along the edge of.

The meadows rolled gently, tilting upward, and their green slope was sprayed with wildflowers. The path crossed a fence, over a rickety stile,[4] then bent and rejoined the brook; and now the cowbells faded and there was again the sound of rushing water. Rudi walked on. Three or four times he passed people going in the opposite direction, but they were only *Ausländer*[5]—tourists—and nothing to worry about. Whatever guides were climbing that day were already high in the mountains. And any others who might have known and questioned him were back in the town or on their farms.

Rudi smiled at the passersby. "*Grüss Gott*,"[6] he said—"God's Greetings"—in the ancient salutation of the Alps.[7] "*Grüss Gott*" they said in reply.

He was no longer hurrying. He walked with the slow, rhythmic pace of the mountain people, and, though the path was now steepening sharply, he felt no strain. His legs, his lungs, all of his slight wiry body, were doing what they did best; what they had been born to do. His feet, through the soles of his shoes, moulded themselves to each hump and crevice[8] of the path. Arms and shoulders swung in easy balance. His breathing was steady, his heartbeat strong and even.

"A typical mountain boy," one would have said, seeing him at a distance. But then, coming closer, one would have seen that he was

4. **stile** [stīl]: a set of steps next to a fence.
5. *Ausländer* [auz′ län dār]
6. *Grüss Gott* [groes got]
7. **Alps:** a chain of mountains extending from the Mediterranean coast between France and Italy into Switzerland. The Alps cover about half of Switzerland.
8. **crevice** [krev′ is]: a narrow split or crack.

not typical at all. Partly, this was because of his slimness, his lightness of muscle and bone; but even more it was in his small, almost delicate features and his fair, pink-and-white complexion. Rudi Matt hated his complexion. In summer he exposed his face for hours to the burning sun, in winter he scrubbed it violently with snow, trying to make it brown and tough and weather-stained, as a mountain man's should be. But no stain appeared. No whisker sprouted. "Angel-face," the other boys called him. Or, rather, *had* called him, until they learned that his fists, though small, were useful. Most of the men of Kurtal[9] had black hair. Rudi's was blond. Most of them had dark eyes. Rudi's were light—though exactly what color no one was quite sure. His mother called them hazel, but she saw them only when he was at home or around the village. When he left the village, when he climbed above it, they seemed to change, as the light changed. Looking up at the great peaks above the valley, they seemed to hold within themselves the gray of mountain rock, the blue of mountain sky.

Rudi Matt climbed on. Now that he was no longer afraid of being stopped, his heart was filled with peace and joy. Just why he had run off on this particular day he could not have said. He had had to—that was all. He had looked from the window of the hotel kitchen and seen the peaks that rimmed the valley rising vast[10] and shining in the morning sun; and he could no more have stopped himself than he could have stopped breathing. A few minutes before, he had been a prisoner. Now he was free. He no longer looked backward—only up—as slowly the great mountain world unfolded before him.

9. **Kurtal** [kėr′ täl]: in this story the name given to the village that is Rudi's home.
10. **vast:** very great, immense.

The path bore away from the brook, zigzagged up the highest of the meadows and entered a forest. And here Rudi stopped. Beside the path, at the forest's edge, was a shrine. It was a tiny thing, no more than a rough wooden box nailed to one of the trees, and inside was a cross and a chipped image of the Virgin. Carved in the wood near the Virgin's feet was the name JOSEF MATT, and beneath it the dates, 1821-1850.

Rudi had never known his father. It had been fifteen years since he had died. But every time in his life that the boy had come to this place he had stopped and prayed. He prayed now, kneeling in the soft moss before the shrine. Then he arose, crossed himself and climbed on through the forest.

A few minutes later he made a second stop. Leaving the path, he made his way between the trees to a large blue spruce and reached for the stout stick that was concealed in its branches. This was his *Alpenstock*,[11] the climber's staff he had made for himself, as a substitute for an ice-ax, which he did not own; and he kept it hidden here because he was afraid that if he took it home his mother or uncle might find it. It was a strong staff, almost five feet long, with a sharp point on one end and a crook[12] on the other. And if it was nothing like the real *Alpenstocks* and axes that Kronig, the smith, made at his forge[13] in the village, at least it was better than nothing. As he hefted it now in his hand, feeling its familiar weight and balance, it was no longer merely a stick, but a part of himself.

He climbed on. For a while, still thinking of his father, he walked slowly and somberly, with his eyes on the ground. But this did not last long, for he was young and the sun was shining and he was doing what he most loved to do in all the world. He tilted his stick before him like a lance.[14] He picked up stones and threw them at the trees. He threw back his head and yodeled and the high wild YOOOO—LEEEE—OOOOO—LAAAY—EEEEE rode the still air like a soaring bird.

11. *Alpenstock* [äl′ pen stok]
12. **crook:** a hook or bend.
13. **forge:** a blacksmith's shop with a furnace where metal is heated and shaped.
14. **lance:** a long wooden spear with a sharp head made of metal.

The path twisted upward. Always upward. The forest was close around him;
then a little less close; then not close at
all. The great firs and spruces fell away,
and he came out onto a slope of dwarf
pine and scraggly, moss-hugging shrubs.
Sitting on a boulder, he ate a bite of
lunch. He had no knapsack, any more
than he had an ice-ax, but he had managed to stuff a piece of bread and another
of cheese into a pocket before bolting[15]
from the hotel kitchen, and, plain and
crumbled though they were, they tasted
better than any food he had ever eaten
in the hotel or in his home.

His eyes moved down across the tree-
tops to the valley. There was the white
thread of the brook dividing it; on either
side the meadows and farms; in the valley's
center the town of Kurtal. He could see
the main street, the square, the church,
the Beau Site Hotel, where he worked,
and the two other hotels beyond it. All
three buildings were new; even Rudi could remember when they had
not been there at all. Ten or twelve years before, Kurtal had been no
more than a tiny farming village, lost in a deep Swiss valley. But while
Rudi had grown, it had grown too. It had become what the *Ausländer*
called a "resort." Each year, during the summer months, there were
more and more visitors—people from the cities, people from England,
France, Germany, and even from faraway America—coming up in the
coaches from the lowlands. In the last few summers there had been so
many of them that there was even talk of building a railway.

It was the mountains that brought them, of course: the tall white
glorious mountains of the Alps. In the old days the people of the

15. **bolting:** dashing off.

outside world had not been interested in the Alps; they had left them to those who had been born and lived there. But in Rudi's own lifetime all that had changed. The *Ausländer* had come: first in trickles, then in droves.[16] They had moved up into the villages, into the high valleys, onto the glaciers, onto the peaks themselves. The sport, the craft, the adventure of mountaineering had been born. In every village, men whose ancestors through all history had been farmers and herdsmen were now farmers and herdsmen no longer, but Alpine guides. And the profession of guide was the proudest in the land. To be a member of the Company of Guides of Kurtal was the highest honor that a man could attain.

Men had not only come to the mountains. They had conquered them. A generation before, only a handful of peaks in the Alps had been climbed to the top, but now, in 1865, there were scarcely any that had *not* been. One by one, year after year, they had been attacked, besieged and taken. Mont Blanc, Monte Rosa, the Dom, the Weisshorn, the Schreckhorn, the Eiger, the Dent Blanche, the Lyskamm[17]—all these and a hundred more, the whole great white host of the most famous mountains of Europe—had felt the boot nails of their conquerors in their summit snows.

All of them . . . except *one*.

Rudi Matt was no longer looking down into the valley. He was looking up and beyond it, and now slowly his eyes moved across the wide circle of the ranges. They moved over the meadows and forests, the glaciers and snowfields, the gorges[18] and precipices,[19] the ridges and peaks. They rested on the snow-dome of Monte Rosa, the spire of the Wunderhorn (his father had first climbed it), the Rotalp[20] (his uncle Franz), the soaring crest of the Weisshorn. Now at last he had

---

16. **droves:** crowds.
17. **Mont Blanc** [mōN′ bläN]; **Monte Rosa** [mänt′ ē rō′ zə]; **Weisshorn** [vīs′ hōrn]; **Shreckhorn** [shrek′ hȯrn]; **Eiger** [ī′ gər]; **Dent Blanche** [däN bläNsh]; **Lyskamm** [lis′ käm]
18. **gorges** [gôrj′ əz]: deep, narrow valleys that are usually steep and rocky.
19. **precipices** [pres′ ə pis əz]: very steep faces of rock.
20. **Wunderhorn** [vün′ där hôrn]; **Rotalp** [rō′ tälp]

turned completely; he was looking in the direction in which he had been climbing. And still his eyes moved on—and up—and up. The other mountains fell away. There was a gap, a deep gorge, a glacier. The earth seemed almost to be gathering itself together. It leaped upward.

And there it was....

The Citadel!

It stood up like a monument: great, terrible—and alone. The other mountains were as nothing beside it. It rose in cliff upon cliff, ridge upon ridge, tower upon tower, until the sharp, curving wedge of its summit seemed to pierce the very heart of the sky. It was a pyramid built up out of a thousand parts—out of granite and limestone[21] and snow and ice, out of glaciers, precipices, crags,[22] ledges, spires, cornices[23]—but so perfect was its vast shape, so harmonious the blending of its elements, that it appeared a single, an organic, almost a living thing. Rudi Matt had been born in its shadow. He had seen it every day of his life. He had stared up at it from the village, from the forests, from the glaciers on every side, until its every detail was fixed indelibly in his mind. But familiarity had not bred indifference. The years had not paled its magic. Instead, that magic had grown stronger, deeper. And on this day, as on every day in his life when he had looked up at it, Rudi Matt felt again the catch in his breath and the wild surging of his heart.

There it stood. The Citadel. The last unconquered summit of the Alps.

"It cannot be climbed," said the people of the valleys. In the past fifteen years no one had even tried to climb it. "It will never be climbed," they said.

No?

*N*ow he was moving on again. He came to a stream, stopped and drank. A furry marmot[24] watched him from a nearby boulder, whistled shrilly and disappeared. High above, a giant hawk whirled slowly through the still, blue air.

Beyond the stream was a fork in the path. The right-hand branch, plain and well trodden, led off toward the Dornelberg[25] and the Wunderhorn, two of the most popular peaks for climbing in the district. But it was not this branch that Rudi followed. Bearing left, he moved on along a barely visible trail that climbed upward toward the base of the Citadel. He was above tree line now. Even the dwarf pine and shrubs were gone—all grass and moss were gone—and the

21. **limestone:** a rock made mostly of calcium carbonate, like marble.
22. **crags:** steep rocks that rise above others.
23. **cornices:** overhanging masses of snow, ice, or rocks.
24. **marmot** [mär′ mət]: a gnawing, burrowing animal related to the squirrel.
25. **Dornelberg** [dôr′ nel bärg]

earth was a bare sweep of gravel and tumbled boulders. Among the boulders the going was tricky, for he had no proper nailed mountain-boots; but his feet were nimble, his balance true, and, making deft[26] use of his self-made staff, he climbed quickly and easily. When, after an hour, he turned and looked back, the rocky point where he had stopped to eat seemed almost as far below him as the village.

The world into which he had now come was one of stillness and desolation. There was the gray of rock, the white of snow, the blue of sky—and that was all there was. The only movement, anywhere, was that of his own body; the only sound the scraping of his own feet against the boulders. Yet Rudi was not conscious of loneliness. He was too used to being alone for that. Every one of the perhaps fifty times during the past two years that he had climbed up to the Citadel's glaciers, he had been alone, and he was now as familiar with this world, and as at home in it, as in the valley below. Pausing now and then, he stared at the mountain that towered gray and monstrous above him. Most of the people in the town believed it was the home of demons, who would destroy anyone who ventured onto its forbidden slopes . . . Well, maybe . . . But he, Rudi, was not yet within a mile of the mountain itself. And if any demons did, indeed, come down into the foothills, they would do so, he was certain, only under cover of night.

He looked up, and the sun was bright and golden in the zenith.[27] The thin finger of cold, that for an instant had touched him, dwindled and was gone.

The slope steepened. The boulders grew larger. He had come to the terminal moraine of the Citadel's glacier—the great mass of tumbled, broken rock which all ice-sheets push and grind before them in their slow descent. Ten more minutes brought him to the top of the moraine, and now the glacier spread before him. Or, more accurately, two glaciers; for he had come out at a point, facing the Kurtal ridge of the Citadel, where its northern and eastern ice-streams met and joined. The one on the north, which was broader,

26. **deft:** nimble, quick and skillful.
27. **zenith** [zē′ nith]: the highest point.

rose to the pass between the Citadel and the Dornelberg and was known as the Dornel Glacier. The eastern one, called the Blue Glacier, was the steeper and climbed like a giant stairway to the saddle—or col[28]—near the base of the Citadel's southeastern ridge. Beyond this col, invisible from where he stood, still another glacier dropped away on the south side of the mountain, toward the valley and village of Broli.[29]

Rudi had ascended both glaciers. He had been to Broli. No less than five times, indeed, he had completely circled the base of the Citadel, climbing up one glacier and down another, traversing the cols and lower ridges, threading his way through the deep, trackless gorges beneath the mountain's western face. He had stared upward until his neck ached and his eyes swam. He had studied every ridge and cliff and ice-wall and ledge and chimney that could be seen from below. He knew more about the approaches to the Citadel than any guide in Kurtal. And yet he still did not know enough. Still he kept coming up to the glaciers to stare again, to

28. **col:** a pass or low spot in a mountain ridge.
29. **Broli** [brō′ lē]

study, to measure. To do this, he had played truant from school— even from church. Now he was running out on his job. Always it meant tears and pleas from his mother, often harsh words from his Uncle Franz. But he did not care. He kept coming back. Nothing in heaven or earth could have held him from coming back.

This time he went up the Blue Glacier. He had not particularly planned to, and just why he picked the Blue, rather than the Dornel, he could not have said. Later, thinking back to that day, he racked his memory for some sign, some motive or portent,[30] that had been the reason for his choice. But he could never find one. He simply crossed the junction of the two ice-streams, bore left, and climbed on toward the south . . . and his destiny.

Like all glaciers, the Blue was cut through by crevasses: deep splits and chasms[31] caused by the pressures of the slow-moving ice. When hidden by snow these could be a great hazard to climbers; but on this midsummer day no snow had fallen in some time, the

30. **portent** [pôr′ tent]: a warning, usually of coming disaster.
31. **chasms** [kaz′ əmz]: deep openings in the earth.

crevasses were plain to view, and there was no danger if one kept his eyes open and paid attention. Rudi zigzagged his way carefully upward. On the ice, of course, his smooth-soled shoes were even worse than on the boulders, but by skillful balancing and use of his stick he kept himself from slipping.

As he climbed, a black dot came into view on the high col ahead. This was an old hut, built many years before by the first explorers of the mountain, but now abandoned and all but forgotten by the people of the valleys. Rudi had twice spent nights there during his circuits of the Citadel, and he knew it well. But it was not there, specifically, that he was going now. He was not going anywhere, specifically, but only climbing, watching, studying. Every few paces now, he would stop and stare upward, motionless.

The east face of the Citadel rose above him like a battlement. Cliff upon cliff, it soared up from the glacier, its rock bulging and bristling,[32] its walls veined with long streaks of ice. Far overhead, he could see a band of snow, which marked the mountain's first setback. Beyond it, the sloping walls disappeared for a space, only to bulge out again higher up—incredibly higher up—in a great gray thrust against the empty sky. So vast was it, so steep, so mighty, that it seemed more than a mere mass of rock and ice. More than a mere mountain. It seemed a new world rising up out of the old world that was its mother; a world with a life and a meaning of its own; beautiful and menacing,[33] beckoning and unknown.

But it was not of beauty or terror that Rudi Matt was thinking as he gazed up at it now from the Blue Glacier. It was of a deep cleft, wide enough for a man's body, that slanted up the rock wall before him—and ended. Of a series of ledges, broad enough for a man's feet, that rose one above another toward the high belt of snow—and petered[34] out. His eyes searched up and down, to the right and the left. He climbed on, stopped, and studied the next section of the face. Then he climbed on again.

32. **bristling:** standing up straight.
33. **menacing** [men′ is ing]: threatening.
34. **petered** [pē′ tərd]: lessened gradually and came to an end.

He moved through absolute silence. Later in the day, when sun and melting snow had done their work, great rock-and-ice masses would break loose from the heights above and come roaring down the mountainside. But it was still too early for this. The Citadel rose up like a tower of iron. There was no movement anywhere. No stirring. No sound.

JAMES RAMSEY ULLMAN

James Ramsey Ullman [1907-1971] was born in New York City. He went to Princeton University and finally made his home in Boston, Massachusetts.

"Home" for Ullman was almost more of a base camp, for he traveled the world in pursuit of mountainous heights. He climbed Mt. Olympus in Greece and the "foothills" of the Andes (many of which are more than sixteen thousand feet high). He also scaled peaks of the Rockies and the Tetons. In 1963, Ullman fulfilled his lifetime dream of being part of the first American expedition to climb Mt. Everest. Two years later, he was involved in another significant historic event: the civil rights freedom march in Montgomery, Alabama.

Ullman began his writing career at twenty-two, as a newspaper reporter and feature writer. Later he began full-time writing, which was to be a life-long passion. Ullman wrote some twenty-two books, many published in England and in foreign translations. He wrote both fiction and nonfiction and contributed to many magazines. His subjects ranged from mountaineering books like *The White Tower* (also a movie) to Caribbean vacation guides.

If you'd like to find out more about Rudi's experiences on the Citadel, look for *Banner in the Sky* in your school or local library.

Painting for Young People Max Ernst, 1943, oil on canvas, 24 $\frac{1}{8}$" X 30 $\frac{1}{8}$", De Menil Foundation, Houston (Details from this painting appear on pages 93, 95, and 97.)

ALL SUMMER IN A DAY

RAY BRADBURY

"Ready?"

"Ready."

"Now?"

"Soon."

"Do the scientists really know? Will it happen today, will it?"

"Look, look; see for yourself!"

The children pressed to each other like so many roses, so many weeds, intermixed, peering out for a look at the hidden sun.

It rained.

It had been raining for seven years; thousands upon thousands of days compounded and filled from one end to the other with rain, with the drum and gush of water, with the sweet crystal fall of showers and the concussion[1] of storms so heavy they were tidal waves come over the islands. A thousand forests had been crushed under the rain and grown up a thousand times to be crushed again. And this was the way life was forever on the planet Venus, and this was the schoolroom of the children of the rocket men and women who had come to a raining world to set up civilization and live out their lives.

"It's stopping, it's stopping!"

"Yes, yes!"

Margot stood apart from them, from these children who could never remember a time when there wasn't rain and rain and rain. They were all nine years old, and if there had been a day, seven years ago, when the sun came out for an hour and showed its face to the stunned world, they could not recall. Sometimes, at night, she heard them stir, in remembrance, and she knew they were dreaming and remembering gold or a yellow crayon or a coin large enough to buy the world with. She knew they thought they remembered a warmness, like a blushing in the face, in the body, in the arms and legs and trembling hands. But then they always awoke to the tatting drum, the endless shaking down of clear bead necklaces upon the roof, the walk, the gardens, the forests, and their dreams were gone.

All day yesterday they had read in class about the sun. About how like a lemon it was, and how hot. And they had written small stories or essays or poems about it:

I think the sun is a flower,
That blooms for just one hour.

That was Margot's poem, read in a quiet voice in the still classroom while the rain was falling outside.

---

1. **concussion** [kən kush′ ən]: a sudden violent shaking.

"Aw, you didn't write that!" protested one of the boys.

"I did," said Margot. "I *did*."

"William!" said the teacher.

But that was yesterday. Now the rain was slackening, and the children were crushed in the great thick windows.

"Where's teacher?"

"She'll be back."

"She'd better hurry, we'll miss it!"

They turned on themselves, like a feverish wheel, all tumbling spokes.

Margot stood alone. She was a very frail girl who looked as if she had been lost in the rain for years and the rain had washed out the blue from her eyes and the red from her mouth and the yellow from her hair. She was an old photograph dusted from an album, whitened away, and if she spoke at all her voice would be a ghost. Now she stood, separate, staring at the rain and the loud wet world beyond the huge glass.

"What're *you* looking at?" said William.

Margot said nothing.

"Speak when you're spoken to." He gave her a shove. But she did not move; rather she let herself be moved only by him and nothing else.

They edged away from her, they would not look at her. She felt them go away. And this was because she would play no games with them in the echoing tunnels of the underground city. If they tagged her and ran, she stood blinking after them and did not follow. When the class sang songs about happiness and life and games her lips barely moved. Only when they sang about the sun and the summer did her lips move as she watched the drenched windows.

And then, of course, the biggest crime of all was that she had come here only five years ago from Earth, and she remembered the sun and the way the sun was and the sky was when she was four in Ohio. And they, they had been on Venus all their lives, and they had been only two years old when last the sun came out and had long since forgotten the color and heat of it and the way it really was. But Margot remembered.

"It's like a penny," she said once, eyes closed.

"No, it's not!" the children cried.

"It's like a fire," she said, "in the stove."

"You're lying, you don't remember!" cried the children.

But she remembered and stood quietly apart from all of them and watched the patterning windows. And once, a month ago, she had refused to shower in the school shower rooms, had clutched her hands to her ears and over her head, screaming the water mustn't touch her head. So after that, dimly, dimly, she sensed it, she was different and they knew her difference and kept away.

There was talk that her father and mother were taking her back to Earth next year; it seemed vital to her that they do so, though it would mean the loss of thousands of dollars to her family. And so, the children hated her for all these reasons of big and little consequence. They hated her pale snow face, her waiting silence, her thinness, and her possible future.

"Get away!" The boy gave her another push. "What're you waiting for?"

Then, for the first time, she turned and looked at him. And what she was waiting for was in her eyes.

"Well, don't wait around here!" cried the boy savagely. "You won't see nothing!"

Her lips moved.

"Nothing!" he cried. "It was all a joke, wasn't it?" He turned to the other children. "Nothing's happening today. *Is* it?"

They all blinked at him and then, understanding, laughed and shook their heads. "Nothing, nothing!"

"Oh, but," Margot whispered, her eyes helpless. "But this is the day, the scientists predict, they say, they *know*, the sun . . ."

"All a joke!" said the boy, and seized her roughly. "Hey, everyone, let's put her in a closet before teacher comes!"

"No," said Margot, falling back.

They surged about her, caught her up and bore her, protesting, and then pleading, and then crying, back into a tunnel, a room, a closet, where they slammed and locked the door. They stood looking at the door and saw it tremble from her beating and throwing herself against it. They heard her muffled cries. Then, smiling, they turned and went out and back down the tunnel, just as the teacher arrived.

"Ready, children?" She glanced at her watch.

"Yes!" said everyone.

"Are we all here?"

"Yes!"

The rain slackened still more.

They crowded to the huge door.

The rain stopped.

It was as if, in the midst of a film concerning an avalanche, a tornado, a hurricane, a volcanic eruption, something had, first, gone wrong with the sound apparatus, thus muffling and finally cutting off all noise, all of the blasts and repercussions and thunders, and then, second, ripped the film from the projector and inserted in its place a peaceful tropical slide which did not move or tremor. The world ground to a standstill. The silence was so immense and unbelievable that you felt your ears had been stuffed or you had lost your hearing altogether. The children put their hands to their ears. They stood apart. The door slid back and the smell of the silent, waiting world came in to them.

The sun came out.

It was the color of flaming bronze and it was very large. And the sky around it was a blazing blue tile color. And the jungle burned with sunlight as the children, released from their spell, rushed out, yelling, into the springtime.

"Now, don't go too far," called the teacher after them. "You've only two hours, you know. You wouldn't want to get caught out!"

But they were running and turning their faces up to the sky and feeling the sun on their cheeks like a warm iron; they were taking off their jackets and letting the sun burn their arms.

"Oh, it's better than the sun lamps, isn't it?"

"Much, much better!"

They stopped running and stood in the great jungle that covered Venus, that grew and never stopped growing, tumultuously,[2] even as you watched it. It was a nest of octopi, clustering up great arms of fleshlike weed, wavering, flowering in this brief spring. It was the color of rubber and ash, this jungle, from the many years without sun. It was the color of stones and white cheeses and ink, and it was the color of the moon.

The children lay out, laughing, on the jungle mattress, and heard it sigh and squeak under them, resilient[3] and alive. They ran among the trees, they slipped and fell, they pushed each other, they played hide-and-seek and tag, but most of all they squinted at the sun until tears ran down their faces, they put their hands up to that yellowness and that amazing blueness and they breathed of the fresh, fresh air and listened and listened to the silence which suspended them in a blessed sea of no sound and no motion. They looked at everything and savored everything. Then, wildly, like animals escaped from their caves, they ran and ran in shouting circles. They ran for an hour and did not stop running.

And then—

In the midst of their running one of the girls wailed.

Everyone stopped.

The girl, standing in the open, held out her hand.

"Oh, look, look," she said, trembling.

They came slowly to look at her opened palm.

In the center of it, cupped and huge, was a single raindrop.

She began to cry, looking at it.

They glanced quietly at the sky.

"Oh. Oh."

2. **tumultuously** [tü mul′ chü əs lē]: violently, roughly.
3. **resilient** [ri zil′ ē′ ənt]: springing back, recovering quickly.

A few cold drops fell on their noses and their cheeks and their mouths. The sun faded behind a stir of mist. A wind blew cool around them. They turned and started to walk back toward the underground house, their hands at their sides, their smiles vanishing away.

A boom of thunder startled them and like leaves before a new hurricane, they tumbled upon each other and ran. Lightning struck ten miles away, five miles away, a mile, a half mile. The sky darkened into midnight in a flash.

They stood in the doorway of the underground for a moment until it was raining hard. Then they closed the door and heard the gigantic sound of the rain falling in tons and avalanches, everywhere and forever.

"Will it be seven more years?"

"Yes. Seven."

Then one of them gave a little cry.

"Margot!"

"What?"

"She's still in the closet where we locked her."

"Margot."

They stood as if someone had driven them, like so many stakes, into the floor. They looked at each other and then looked away. They glanced out at the world that was raining now and raining and raining steadily. They could not meet each other's glances. Their faces were solemn and pale. They looked at their hands and feet, their faces down.

"Margot."

One of the girls said, "Well . . .?"

No one moved.

"Go on," whispered the girl.

They walked slowly down the hall in the sound of cold rain. They turned through the doorway to the room in the sound of the storm and thunder, lightning

on their faces, blue and terrible. They walked over to the closet door slowly and stood by it.

Behind the closet door was only silence.

They unlocked the door, even more slowly, and let Margot out.

Sun and Forest Max Ernst, 1926, oil on canvas, 26" X 32 ½", Richard Zeisler Collection, New York

RAY BRADBURY

Ray Bradbury was born in 1920 in Waukegan, Illinois, and started writing as a young child. Comic book adventures sparked his interest in what he calls "the fabulous world of the future, and the world of fantasy." His first work was done on a toy typewriter given to him for Christmas by his parents. "I stormed it with words," he says. "Anytime I liked, I could turn a faucet on each finger and let the miracles out into machines and onto paper where I might freeze and control them forever."

Bradbury wrote his first Martian stories when he was twelve. His "faucet fingers" never failed him. Bradbury has written a great many stories and several novels.

Most of his adventure, however, has been through writing. He has confessed that though his characters inhabit strange planets and fly through space without fear, he hates airplanes.

FRANCES FROST

Valentine for Earth

Oh, it will be fine
To rocket through space
And see the reverse
Of the moon's dark face,

To travel to Saturn   5
Or Venus or Mars,
Or maybe discover
Some uncharted stars.

But do they have anything   10
Better than we?
Do you think, for instance,
They have a blue sea
For sailing and swimming?
Do planets have hills   15
With raspberry thickets
Where a song sparrow fills

The summer with music?
And do they have snow
To silver the roads   20
Where the school buses go?

Oh, I'm all for rockets
And worlds cold or hot,
But I'm wild in love
With the planet we've got!

FRANCES FROST

Frances Frost was born in 1905 in St. Albans, Vermont, and started writing when she was in the eighth grade. Around a life of travel, family-raising, teaching, and (at one time) driving a taxi, she found time to write short stories.

Frost published a number of short stories before she began to write poems. She has created poetry collections and novels for both adults and children. However, it is her poetry that has won her the most honors. As one critic put it, "hers is the sort of poetry that expresses the thoughts everyday people have" and she puts those thoughts on paper the way others would if they could.

Asking Big Questions About the Literature

What are some favorite places people have?

LITERATURE STUDY

Setting

Setting is the time and place of a work of literature. Look around! The literature in this unit offers a wide variety of settings. Each is a favorite or frightening place for one or more of the main characters in a story or novel, for the speaker of a poem, or for the writer of an essay. Make an overview chart like the one shown of the time and place in each selection you've read. (*See "Setting" on page 118.*)

Literature	Time	Place
"Go Home"	present	a farm with a barn and fields

Illustrator for Hire!

Choose one of the places that you enjoyed most in this unit. Imagine that you work for a publisher and that you've been asked to illustrate the story, essay, or poem. Make your illustration capture a single moment in time. Give it a caption that is a sentence or line from the literature. Display your illustration in your classroom.

Write a

POSTCARD

Imagine that you are one of the characters in this unit. Design and write a postcard that shows your strange or special place. On one side, illustrate a place in the story. On the other side, write a message about that place. Address the card to someone in your class. Include a postmark and post the card on a bulletin board for class mail.

What makes a place special?

Sensory Language

Writers work hard to make readers feel as though they are right in the middle of the settings. They don't just *tell* about time and place. They *show* the settings by using **sensory language.** Such language uses a rich variety of details such as sights, sounds, tastes, smells, and touches. Choose three selections that you enjoyed and fill in a sensory chart, like the one shown, for the most important setting in each selection you choose. Here's the beginning of such a chart for "The Secret Among the Stones." (*See "Sensory Language" on page 119.*)

"The Secret Among the Stones"	
Sight	A dim, dark cave
Sound	slithery sounds of a snake
Smell	snuffy, acrid smell
Taste	
Touch	

Write a COMPARISON

Choose two pieces of literature in this unit that have very different settings. In a letter to a friend who has not read the unit, compare and contrast the two settings. Remember that a comparison shows how the settings are alike. A contrast shows how the settings are different. Explain why you like the two settings and why they are special to the character(s). In your letter, encourage your friend to read the two selections.

Take A FIELD TRIP

Your class can take a field trip to one of the settings in this unit by making a mural. First you must decide on your destination. Discuss the pros and cons of each selection's setting. Then vote to narrow down your choices to one. Include as many vivid details as possible in your mural.

Asking Big Questions About the Literature

Why do people seek strange and special places?

LITERATURE STUDY

Sensory Language

In many pieces of literature, the settings change from one part of a story to another. Choose a selection from this unit in which a character moves from place to place, and draw a story map showing how the settings change. In the map, use **sensory language** that gives details of sight, sound, smell, taste, and touch to describe each setting. Use the map that was started for "A Brother's Promise" as a model. (*See "Sensory Language" on page 119.*)

Find the Reasons

In your journal, answer this Big Question for each poem in this unit, using a phrase to describe the speakers if you don't know their names. Make your answers as detailed as possible. When you're finished, read your answers to a partner and listen as your partner reads his or her answers. How do the answers differ?

Write a
NEWS STORY

Turn the events of one of the selections into a newspaper story. Make sure your news story answers the questions *who, what, when, where, why,* and *how.* Create a large headline using a form of the word *seek* and display your news story on a bulletin board. You might arrange to read the story aloud as if it were a radio broadcast.

cold blustery morning in Madison Square, up in the statue

the dinner table under the chandelier in 1884

How do people react to strange and special places?

LITERATURE STUDY

Setting

Setting, the time and place of a work of literature, usually has a strong effect on the characters. Look back on the main characters in four literature selections in this unit. Fill in a chart like the one below that shows how the characters react when they are in the strange or special place. (*See "Setting" on page 118.*)

Write a SONG

Songs and poems often show strong feelings. Choose one of the prose selections from this unit and write a poem about the special place at its center. Set your poem to music if you feel inspired. As a class, share your original poems and songs.

PLAY a Role

Role-play a character in one of the selections describing to a friend the strange or special place in the selection. Try to make the friend feel as if he or she is there by including how the place makes the character feel. The description should be lively and specific.

Literature	"Under the Back Porch"
Character	the speaker in the poem
Place	under the porch
Feelings	security, peace

NOW Choose a Project!

Three projects involving special places are described on the following pages.

Writing Workshop

STOP AT OUR PLACE

Prewriting
....
THINKING OF PLACES

What are some favorite places people have in your city, town, or neighborhood? Your **purpose** in this project is to design, write, and publish a brochure describing six to ten of those favorite places. People who may be visiting your area for the first time will be your **audience.** They might pick up a copy of the brochure at the bus station or the Chamber of Commerce and decide what places they'll want to see. You might even include a few photographs and a map to make your brochure more appealing.

The first step is to brainstorm a list of possible places in your community that you might include. It may help to think about these questions as you brainstorm.

- Where are the best places to eat?
- Have any famous people lived here?
- Are there any famous historical events or sites?
- Are there any unique or special stores or museums?
- What's the oldest building around? The newest?
- Are there any big lakes, mountains, rivers, dams, waterfalls?
- What's *your* favorite place? Why?

After you've brainstormed your list, step back and narrow it down. Choose six to ten places that you think visitors would most enjoy. Include a variety of places rather than seven stores and one restaurant. And recommend a place that's just for fun—some place unexpected and unique.

Prewriting
GATHERING DETAILS

There are many ways to gather specific details about the places you've chosen to describe. Here are a few suggestions:

- For each place, write a few sentences about what makes the place special. Why might people want to visit it? Use your sentences to guide your thinking as you gather your details.
- Visit each place with your notebook in hand. If you can't visit, trust your memory. If you've never been there and can't go there, omit that place from your brochure. Make a sensory chart like the one on page 103 for each place and include as many details as you can.
- Take photographs or make sketches.
- Ask someone who works at each place for information that might interest tourists. For example, when did the restaurant first open? How many books does the library hold? Who built that antique house?
- Talk to older people who know the places well. Maybe they'll offer an amusing story or a unique detail. You might jot down a quotation or two that you can use.
- Make sure you get the correct address and phone number of each place to include in your brochure. Can you find a small map of your area and mark each of the locations on it?

Writing Workshop

Drafting YOUR DESCRIPTIONS

Decide in what order you want your descriptions to appear. You might use your map as a guide. As you draft a strong descriptive paragraph or two for each place, keep these strategies in mind.

- Write a strong introduction to your paragraph. Include several sensory details about the place and a snappy conclusion.
- Try putting your details in spatial order. Words like *next to*, *left to right*, and *top to bottom* help readers get a clear picture of a place.
- Use strong, specific nouns and sharp verbs. Use crisp language that is short and to the point. For example, instead of *a lot of big tall trees*, write *forest* or *woods*.
- Appeal to more than one sense. Don't just rely on the sense of sight. Describing the smell of fresh-baked bread may attract more visitors to a restaurant than describing its stained glass windows.
- Vary the way you express ideas. Look at advertising language for tips. Advertisers use short catchy phrases, ask questions, make exclamations. Use these examples as models.

Come one, come all! Apple picking time!

Breathe that ocean air!

Want to buy a 1967 Reggie Jackson in mint condition?

- Include all essential information. Don't forget to include information tourists will need. For example, it won't help them to know about the oldest log cabin in the country if they don't know where it's located or what hours it's open for tours.
- Write a brief introduction to your brochure. After you've written all the descriptions, write a few sentences that introduce tourists to your area and lead into the descriptions. You have a chance to be creative here and pretend you're a tour guide or travel agent.

Revising YOUR DESCRIPTIONS

- Read your descriptions out loud—either to yourself, a partner, or group. Listen for awkward phrases and unnecessary words. Can you substitute short, crisp language for any long phrases?
- Is each description unique and colorful? Be careful of adjectives like *great, fun, interesting,* and *wonderful.* Use a dictionary or thesaurus to find fresh words to replace overused words.
- Is the order appropriate? Remember that the first and last place in the brochure should be the strongest attractions for visitors.
- How well do the descriptions work with the drawings or photographs you've chosen? Does an illustration or photo need a caption? If a detail is clearly shown in a photograph, maybe there's no need to include it in the description.

Editing YOUR DESCRIPTIONS

As always, have someone else proofread your descriptions for grammatical, mechanical, and spelling errors. Pay particular attention to the spelling of place names and to punctuation. Offer to proofread someone else's work in return.

Publishing YOUR BROCHURE

If possible, use a word processor to publish your brochure. If you prefer, hand letter the descriptions carefully in ink. Format the paragraphs to fit below, above, or beside the illustrations.

Give your brochure a catchy title and decide how it will open and fold up. Perhaps you can show a copy to your local Chamber of Commerce, town office, or tourist information center. Or maybe they can work with you, offering suggestions as the project progresses. At least mail copies to out-of-town friends to convince them to come for a visit!

A student's description of highlights in her community is on pages 110 and 111. Are there any places in your community like them?

STUDENT MODEL

Visit St. Charles, Illinois

by Paula K. Ligler
of St. Charles, Illinois

Good morning, ladies and gentlemen; welcome to St. Charles—a very captivating place to visit. This town of 23,000 people is full of exciting activities. The Fox River and the historical landmarks and legends play a big role in St. Charles life. Let me take you on a magical bus ride around St. Charles so you can see just how beautiful it really is.

Today we will be visiting the Kane County Flea Market, which you will see in a few moments as we enter the Kane County

Fairgrounds. We will be spending two breathtaking hours exploring the antiques. Before you exit, let me tell you about the Flea Market.

Kane County Flea Market is the world's biggest flea market. It draws hundreds of people to St. Charles on the first Sunday of every month. This market shows almost every antique imaginable— from coffee tables to dried flowers. You can see the dried flowers on our left. The market is open all year, no matter what the weather. Even though we can't experience a full day at the Kane County Flea Market, I hope you will enjoy a fun-filled time as you browse through all the dealers' displays.

Once we leave the Flea Market, our destination will be another antiques bonanza located in downtown St. Charles. There are three antique markets where you will find everything you need, from jewelry to furniture. Even Hollywood prop directors and set decorators come to St. Charles for authentic clothing and furniture for hit movies. I know you'll enjoy these shops! After an hour of shopping, we will be off to lunch. You may take your pick of St. Charles's very quaint restaurants.

· ·

I hope you enjoyed your lunch. Let's board our bus now and spend the rest of the afternoon enjoying many exciting activities in Pottawatomie Park. The name Pottawatomie is Native American and refers to those native people who once settled here. During our

visit, you may take a walk along the well-known Fox River. On your walk, you will come across a statue of a chief of the Pottawatomie tribe.

Another way to see the Fox River from this park is to take a relaxing ride on the spacious paddle boat, where you can sightsee four miles of the river. Incidentally, the Fox River is a main source of activities in St. Charles, such as fast-paced canoe rides and the "Pride of the Fox"—a festival held every year featuring a carnival. Have fun!

Now that we have come to the final minutes of this tour, I would like to thank you for being a great audience. I hope you have had fun today in St. Charles.

Cooperative Learning

DESIGNERS AT WORK

Have you ever wished you could design the park, playground, or fun house of your dreams? What would it include? Where would it be located? What would people do there? Well, now's your chance! In this project, you and a group of three to six others will design this special place and then make a visual, written, and oral presentation of your plans to your classmates. So, start dreaming, start talking, and start listening.

The PROCESS

Step 1: Brainstorming   Begin with a group brainstorming session. Remember that there's no limit to what you can do! At this point, assign a recorder to write everything down in a large chart. You can pick and choose specific ideas later.

Step 2: Making a Choice   Have each member add ideas to existing suggestions. When you've run out of ideas, work to make a choice. Then put the list to a simple vote or use discussion to move the group toward favoring one project.

Step 3: Planning and Assigning Tasks
Once you've decided on a project, a location, and a purpose, start planning. Questions such as these might help.

Project	park
Location	Sandy Beach
Purpose	family picnics
Parts	tables, playground, swimming area,

- How will people get there?
- How will people enter and exit?
- How much area will this place require?
- What will its various parts be?
- What will it be called?

Now, divide your team into three groups. Each group will be responsible for one kind of presentation: visual, written, and oral. But don't stop working together. All three parts must describe the same place. Keep in constant communication. Discuss any specific details and make sure you all agree before you use them in your presentations.

The PRESENTATION

Once you've finished your plans, create a three-dimensional presentation for your classmates.

The Visual Representation   Make a scale model of your special place—an architectural drawing (a blueprint or floor plan) or a color illustration of what the finished place will look like. Make the visual big enough to be displayed somewhere in your school.

The Written Description   Write a paragraph or essay about the place you've imagined. Individual paragraphs could describe the various parts. Appeal to the five senses and be as specific as possible.

The Oral Presentation   Use the visuals and written descriptions as aids. Team members also may answer any classmates' questions. Display the visual and written parts of your projects in your school for everyone to see. Who knows? Maybe a local architect will be interested too!

PROJECT 3

CLEANUP TIME

Helping Your Community

You and your classmates can make a special place even more special by organizing a voluntary cleanup effort. This project will show you how.

Choose THE PLACE AND TIME

Brainstorm a list of several places you might clean up. Discuss the pros and cons of each place before choosing one through a class vote. Then think hard about the place you chose. Is it a good choice? Why or why not?

Pick a day and time for the cleanup. What's best? A weekday? A weekend? Morning? Evening? Why? See if you can reach a consensus about a date and time. Next think of a rain date and time in case of bad weather.

Organize THE CLEANUP

Call local authorities Make sure that your plans are cleared with the people in charge. Community officials who should know about your effort are the police department, the sanitation or recycling department, and the office that governs the public place you plan to clean up. Contact the offices either by phone or by mail (at least three weeks ahead of your planned cleanup day) and let them know what you hope to do. Ask them for advice or suggestions. Listen carefully and follow all of their instructions.

Develop an action plan What will happen when cleanup volunteers arrive at the site? If possible, ask a local merchant to donate garbage bags or have volunteers bring their own. What will be done with the full bags? Make plans with your local sanitation department or recycling department for trash collection.

Police Dept.	
Internal Affairs	555-3318
Parking Ticket Info	555-4705
Stolen Vehicles	555-3301
Traffic Division	555-3305
Public Works Dept.	
Info. & General Services	555-4800
Recycling Hotline	555-4005
City Architect Ofc.	555-4815
City Engineer Ofc.	555-4829
Parks & Forestry Div.	555-4880
Pot Hole Complaint Line	555-4854
Sanitation/Street Sweeping	555-4849

Have volunteers wear gloves. Will you need other cleanup equipment? Buckets and sponges? Rakes? Brooms? Plan ahead. Good organization will make the day go smoothly.

Tasks	Persons Responsible
1. Make contacts	
2. Equipment	
3. Trash Collection	

Publicize the cleanup Make posters and flyers and hang them in your school, the library, or any public place. Distribute flyers to other classes. The more people who volunteer, the better and more efficient the effort will be.

Contact the local newspaper and ask them to cover the event. Perhaps they can take "before" and "after" photographs. You can do a good deed and be famous at the same time!

On the day of the cleanup, bring plenty of water for people to drink. Music or even live entertainment may make the day complete. Perhaps a local merchant will donate treats such as apples, lollipops, badges, or certificates. At the finish, post a sign to encourage future users to keep the place free of litter and congratulate the volunteers!

Metro/Region

LOCAL STUDENTS CLEANUP PLAYGROUND

Saturday morning dawned bright and sunny for the Bridge Middle School's first annual city park cleanup. Sixth graders arrived fully prepared with gloves and rakes. They also had recycle bags and bi

Putting It All Together

What Have You Learned About Strange and Special Places?

Now that you've finished *Strange and Special Places*, think about how your ideas about this theme may have changed. Look back at some of the journal writing you did before you read the literature in this unit and choose one place you mentioned. Write a descriptive paragraph about that place. Then combine your description with those of your classmates into a collection called "Our Favorite Places."

A PLACE FOR ME

Prewriting and Drafting   Brainstorm about the meaning of this strange or special place in your life. Make a detailed sensory chart like the one on page 103 to explore the various sensory details you observe about your place. Then list the emotions you experience when you are in this place. Use the chart for the journal activity on page 11 as your model.

Now your job is to make your readers experience this place as if they are *there*— just as the authors of the literature in this unit did for you. First imagine that you are approaching this place and begin your paragraph by introducing your readers to the place. Be dramatic so the reader will pay attention! Then imagine you are walking slowly through the place and describe it. Take your time and build your description with sensory details of color, sound, smell, texture and touch, and taste—if appropriate. Use specific nouns, lively verbs, and colorful adjectives in your sentences. In your conclusion, write about the emotions you feel about this place.

Revising and Editing   Read your description to your partner or a writing group. Can anyone clearly see the place and follow in your footsteps? Are there any confusing sections? Pay attention to suggestions for improvement. After revising, ask your partner or group to check the grammar, punctuation, and spelling.

Publishing   With your classmates, create a cover for your anthology of descriptions about places and try to exhibit the collection in the classroom or school library.

Evaluating Your Work

Think Back About the Big Questions

With a partner, discuss the Big Questions about special places on pages 10 and 11. In your journal, write two or three sentences discussing how your responses to the Big Questions have changed after your work in this unit.

Think Back About Your Work

Now think about the unit you've just finished and evaluate your work, including your reading, your writing, your activities, and your projects. Be kind to yourself, but be honest too!

Write a note to your favorite relative. In your note, explain what you've done during this unit and what you've learned. Use the following questions to help you write your note.

- What literature selections in this unit affected you most strongly? Why?

- What was your favorite activity in this unit? Why?

- What was you least favorite activity? Why?

- If you were to do your project again, what parts would you do the same way? What parts would you do differently?

- What did you learn as you worked on your project?

- What have you learned in this unit about strange and special places?

- How would you rate your work in this unit? Use the following scale and give at least three reasons for your rating.

  1 = Outstanding   3 = Fair
  2 = Good   4 = Not as good as it could have been

SETTING

What Is Setting?

Setting is the time and place of a work of literature. A writer literally creates an environment by using carefully selected details. These details outline the geographical location, the season of the year, the weather, the time of day, the outdoor location, the inside of a building or a room, the historical period, or any other conditions of a particular time and place. A writer often uses setting to create a *mood*—an *atmosphere* or *feeling*—and, sometimes, to create a *conflict* for a character, such as when a person has to struggle to survive in a wilderness setting.

Writing a Letter   When you read a selection, it may seem so real that you think you are a part of the story. Imagine that you're away from home, visiting a setting in one of the selections. In a letter, tell others about the place you're visiting. Write a letter to a friend or relative about a setting from one of the selections you read in this unit. In your own words, try to recreate the setting. You want to convince your audience that this is a special or scary place. As part of the letter, ask the person who reads it to draw your setting from the description you've provided. Finally invite that person to read the selection and discuss it with you.

Becoming a Tour Guide   Imagine you are a guide on a bus tour. Prepare a script that you'll use to acquaint visitors with a setting of your choice. First, collect information—which could be interesting stories—about the place(s) you've chosen to describe. For each place, record details on an index card. Then using those cards, practice delivering your facts to the bus passengers. You'll want to entertain as well as inform your audience. Finally present a dramatic reading of your script to your classmates.

What Is Sensory Language?

Sensory language is language that uses rich details of sight, sound, smell, touch, and taste to describe a person, place, or thing. Writers know that people experience the world through their senses. Therefore, a good writer selects certain details and creates words and phrases of color, sound, taste, and texture to describe these details. For instance, a hot day becomes the "orange boil that scorched the hours." If the writer succeeds, the reader can more easily imagine and enjoy the world the writer has created.

Discovering Sensory Language In a short story, sensory language is especially important because the writer tries to provide a description using the fewest possible words and phrases. Choose one of your favorite short stories in this unit. In your journal, write at least five examples of sensory language that the writer uses to describe the setting or characters. Then try to put these examples into categories of sight, sound, smell, touch, or taste. Finally, use the examples as models as you write a description of a place that is special to you.

Writing a Poem Every day, from the second you wake up until the moment you fall asleep, your senses collect and process information about the world around you. Some places are quiet and still. Others are noisy and busy. Choose a place that's full of sights and sounds, such as a crowded restaurant, a busy store, a carnival, a sports event, or a concert. In your journal, make a sensory chart like the one shown on page 103 and record those specific sensory details that are unique to that place. Try to think of at least three details for each sense. Then write a poem about the place, using sensory language to make your setting come alive.

GLOSSARY OF LITERARY TERMS

A

alliteration   Repetition of the first sound—usually a consonant sound—in several words of a sentence or a line of poetry.

allusion   An author's indirect reference to someone or something that is presumed to be familiar to the reader.

anecdote   A short narrative about an interesting or humorous event, usually in the life of a person.

antagonist   The person or force opposing the protagonist or main character in a literary work. [See also *protagonist*.]

autobiography   A person's written account of his or her own life.

B

ballad   A poem, often a song, that tells a story in simple verse.

biography   An account of a person's life, written by another person.

blank verse   Unrhymed poetry.

C

character   A person or an animal that participates in the action of a work of literature. A *dynamic character* is one whose thoughts, feelings, and actions are changeable and lifelike; a *static character* always remains the same. [See also *protagonist, antagonist*.]

characterization   The creation of characters through the characters' use of language and through descriptions of their appearance, thoughts, emotions, and actions. [See also *character*.]

chronology   An arrangement of events in the order in which they happen.

cliché   An overused expression that sounds trite rather than meaningful.

climax   The highest point of tension in the plot of a work of literature. [See also *plot*.]

comedy   An amusing play that has a happy ending.

conclusion   The final part or ending of a piece of literature.

concrete poem   A poem arranged on the page so that its punctuation, letters, and lines make the shape of the subject of the poem.

conflict   A problem that confronts the characters in a piece of literature. The conflict may be *internal* (a character's struggle within himself or herself) or *external* (a character's struggle against nature, another person, or society). [See also *plot*.]

context   The general sense of words that helps readers to understand the meaning of unfamiliar words and phrases in a piece of writing.

D

description   An author's use of words to give the reader or listener a mental picture, impression, or understanding of a person, place, thing, event, or idea.

dialect   A form of speech spoken by people in a particular group or geographical region that differs in vocabulary, grammar, and pronunciation from the standard language.

dialogue   The spoken words and conversation of characters in a work of literature.

drama   A play that is performed before an audience according to stage directions and using dialogue. Classical drama has two genres: *tragedy* and *comedy*. Modern drama includes *melodrama, satire, theater of the absurd,* and *pantomime*. [See also *comedy, play,* and *tragedy*.]

dramatic poetry   A play written in the form of poetry.

E

epic   A long narrative poem written in a formal style and meant to be read aloud that relates the adventures and experiences of one or more great heroes or heroines.

essay Personal nonfiction writing about a particular subject that is important to the writer.

excerpt A passage from a larger work that has been taken out of its context to be used for a special purpose.

exposition Writing that explains, analyzes, or defines.

extended metaphor An elaborately drawn out metaphor. [See also *metaphor*.]

F

fable A short, simple story whose purpose is to teach a lesson, usually with animal characters who talk and act like people.

fantasy Imaginative fiction about unrealistic characters, places, and events.

fiction Literature, including the short story and the novel, that tells about imaginary people and events.

figurative language Language used to express ideas through figures of speech: descriptions that aren't meant to be taken literally. Types of figurative language include *simile, metaphor, extended metaphor, hyperbole,* and *personification.*

figure of speech A type of figurative language, not meant to be taken literally, that expresses something in such a way that it brings the thing to life in the reader's or listener's imagination. [See also *figurative language*.]

flashback A break in a story's action that relates a past happening in order to give the reader background information about a present action in the story.

folktale A story that has been passed along from storyteller to storyteller for generations. Kinds of folktales include *tall tales, fairy tales, fables, legends,* and *myths.*

foreshadowing The use of clues to create suspense by giving the reader or audience hints of events to come.

free verse Poetry that has no formal rhyme scheme or metrical pattern.

G

genre A major category of art. The three major literary genres are poetry, prose, and drama.

H

haiku A three-line Japanese verse form. In most haiku, the first and third lines have five syllables, while the second line has seven. The traditional haiku describes a complicated feeling or thought in simple language through a single image.

hero/heroine The main character in a work of literature. In heroic literature, the hero or heroine is a particularly brave, noble, or clever person whose achievements are unusual and important. [See also *character*.]

heroic age The historical period in western civilization—from about 800 B.C. through A.D. 200—during which most works of heroic literature, such as myths and epics, were created in ancient Greece and Rome.

hubris Arrogance or excessive pride leading to mistakes; the character flaw in a hero of classical tragedy.

hyperbole An obvious exaggeration used for emphasis. [See also *figurative language*.]

I

idiom An expression whose meaning cannot be understood from the ordinary meaning of the words. For example, *It's raining cats and dogs.*

imagery The words and phrases in writing that appeal to the senses of sight, hearing, taste, touch, and smell.

irony   An effect created by a sharp contrast between what is expected and what is real. An *ironic twist* in a plot is an event that is the complete opposite of what the characters have been hoping or expecting will happen. An *ironic statement* declares the opposite of the speaker's literal meaning.

J

jargon   Words and phrases used by a group of people who share the same profession or special interests in order to refer to technical things or processes with which they are familiar. In general, jargon is any terminology that sounds unclear, overused, or pretentious.

L

legend   A famous folktale about heroic actions, passed along by word of mouth from generation to generation. The legend may have begun as a factual account of real people and events but has become mostly or completely fictitious.

limerick   A form of light verse, or humorous poetry, written in one five-line stanza with a regular scheme of rhyme and meter.

literature   The branch of art that is expressed in written language and includes all written genres.

lyric poem   A short poem that expresses personal feelings and thoughts in a musical way. Originally, lyrics were the words of songs that were sung to music played on the lyre, a stringed instrument invented by the ancient Greeks.

M

metamorphosis   The transformation of one thing, or being, into another completely different thing or being, such as a caterpillar's change into a butterfly.

metaphor   Figurative language in which one thing is said to be another thing. [See also *figurative language*.]

meter   The pattern of rhythm in lines of poetry. The most common meter, in poetry written in English, is iambic pentameter, that is, a verse having five metrical feet, each foot of verse having two syllables, an unaccented one followed by an accented one.

mood   The feeling or atmosphere that a reader senses while reading or listening to a work of literature.

motivation   A character's reasons for doing, thinking, feeling, or saying something. Sometimes an author will make a character's motivation obvious from the beginning. In realistic fiction and drama, however, a character's motivation may be so complicated that the reader discovers it gradually, by studying the character's thoughts, feelings, and behavior.

myth   A story, passed along by word of mouth for generations, about the actions of gods and goddesses or superhuman heroes and heroines. Most myths were first told to explain the origins of natural things or to justify the social rules and customs of a particular society.

N

narration   The process of telling a story. For both fiction and nonfiction, there are two main kinds of narration, based on whether the story is told from first-person or third-person point of view. [See also *point of view*.]

narrative poem   A poem that tells a story containing the basic literary ingredients of fiction: character, setting, and plot.

narrator   The person, or voice, that tells a story. [See also *point of view, voice*.]

nonfiction   Prose that is factually true and is about real people, events, and places.

nonstandard English
Versions of English, such as slang and dialects, that use pronunciation, vocabulary, idiomatic expressions, grammar, and punctuation that differ from the accepted "correct" constructions of English.

novel   A long work of narrative prose fiction. A novel contains narration, a setting or settings, characters, dialogue, and a more complicated plot than a short story.

O

oral tradition   Stories, poems, and songs that have been kept alive by being told, recited, and sung by people over many generations. Since the works were not originally written, they often have many different versions.

onomatopoeia   The technique of using words that imitate the sounds they describe, such as *hiss*, *buzz*, and *splash*.

P

parable   A brief story, similar to a fable, but about people, that describes an ordinary situation and concludes with a short moral or lesson to be learned.

personification   Figurative language in which an animal, an object, or an idea is given human characteristics. [See also *figurative language*.]

persuasion   A type of speech or writing whose purpose is to convince people that something is true or important.

play   A work of dramatic literature written for performance by actors before an audience. In classical or traditional drama, a play is divided into five acts, each containing a number of scenes. Each act represents a distinct phase in the development of the plot. Modern plays often have only one act and one scene.

playwright   The author of a play.

plot   The sequence of actions and events in fiction or drama. A traditional plot has at least three parts: the *rising action*, leading up to a turning point that affects the main character; the *climax*, the turning point or moment of greatest intensity or interest; and the *falling action*, leading away from the conflict, or resolving it.

poetry   Language selected and arranged in order to say something in a compressed or nonliteral way. Modern poetry may or may not use many of the traditional poetic techniques that include *meter*, *rhyme*, *alliteration*, *figurative language*, *symbolism*, and *specific verse forms*.

point of view   The perspective from which a writer tells a story. *First-person* narrators tell the story from their own point of view, using pronouns like *I* or *me*. *Third-person* narrators, using pronouns like *he*, *she*, or *them*, may be *omniscient* (knowing everything about all characters), or *limited* (taking the point of view of one character). [See also *narration*.]

propaganda   Information or ideas that may or may not be true, but are spread as though they are true, in order to persuade people to do or believe something.

prose   The ordinary form of written and spoken language used to create fiction, nonfiction, and most drama.

protagonist   The main character of a literary work. [See also *character* and *characterization*.]

R

refrain   A line or group of lines that is repeated, usually at the end of each verse, in a poem or a song.

repetition   The use of the same formal element more than once in a literary work, for emphasis or in order to achieve another desired effect.

resolution   The "falling action" in fiction or drama,

including all of the developments that follow the climax and show that the story's conflict is over. [See also *plot*.]

rhyme scheme   A repeated pattern of similar sounds, usually found at the ends of lines of poetry or poetic drama.

rhythm   In poetry, the measured recurrence of accented and unaccented syllables in a particular pattern. [See also *meter*.]

S

scene   The time, place, and circumstances of a play or a story. In a play, a scene is a section of an act. [See also *play*.]

science fiction   Fantasy literature set in an imaginary future, with details and situations that are designed to seem scientifically possible.

setting   The time and place of a work of literature.

short story   Narrative prose fiction that is shorter and has a less complicated plot than a novel. A short story contains narration, at least one setting, at least one character, and usually some dialogue.

simile   Figurative language that compares two unlike things, introduced by the words "like" or "as." [See also *figurative language*.]

soliloquy   In a play, a short speech spoken by a single character when he or she is alone on the stage. A soliloquy usually expresses the character's innermost thoughts and feelings, when he or she thinks no other characters can hear.

sonnet   A poem written in one stanza, using fourteen lines of iambic pentameter. [See also *meter*.]

speaker   In poetry, the individual whose voice seems to be speaking the lines. [See also *narration, voice*.]

stage directions   The directions, written by the playwright, to tell the director, actors, and theater technicians how a play should be dramatized. Stage directions may specify such things as how the setting should appear in each scene, how the actors should deliver their lines, when the stage curtain should rise and fall, how stage lights should be used, where on the stage the actors should be during the action, and when sound effects should be used.

stanza   A group of lines in poetry set apart by blank lines before and after the group; a poetic verse.

style   The distinctive way in which an author composes a work of literature in written or spoken language.

suspense   An effect created by authors of various types of fiction and drama, especially adventure and mystery plots, to heighten interest in the story.

symbol   An image, person, place, or thing that is used to express the idea of something else.

T

tall tale   A kind of folk tale, or legend, that exaggerates the characteristics of its hero or heroine.

theme   The main idea or underlying subject of a work of literature.

tone   The attitude that a work of literature expresses to the reader through its style.

tragedy   In classical drama, a tragedy depicts a noble hero or heroine who makes a mistake of judgment that has disastrous consequences.

V

verse   A stanza in a poem. Also, a synonym for poetry as a genre. [See also *stanza*.]

voice   The narrator or the person who relates the action of a piece of literature. [See also *speaker*.]

ACKNOWLEDGMENTS

Grateful acknowledgment is made for permission to reprint the following copyrighted material.

"Under the Back Porch" by Virginia Hamilton is reprinted from *Home*, edited by Michael Rosen, copyright © 1992 by Virginia Hamilton, by permission of the author.

"Rulers of Terabithia" from *Bridge to Terabithia* by Katherine Paterson, copyright © 1977 by Katherine Paterson, is used by permission of HarperCollins Publishers.

"The Secret Among the Stones" by Ardath Mayhar is reprinted by permission from *Within Reach*, edited by Don Gallo, HarperCollins Publishers, copyright ©1993.

"The Cave" by Glenn W. Dresbach is reprinted from *Collected Poems* by Glenn Ward Dresbach by permission of The Caxton Printers, Ltd., Caldwell, Idaho.

"The Cave" by Enrique Jaramillo Levi is reprinted by permission from *Where Angels Glide at Dawn: New Stories from Latin America*, copyright © 1990 by Lori Carlson and Cynthia Ventura

"A Brother's Promise" by Pam Conrad is reprinted by permission from *Within Reach*, edited by Don Gallo, copyright ©1993, HarperCollins Publisher.

"The Lightwell" by Laurence Yep, copyright ©1992 by Laurence Yep is reproduced by permission of Laurence Yep and Curtis Brown, Ltd.

"Grandmama's Kitchen Table" by Cynthia Rylant, copyright © 1992, is reprinted from *Home* by HarperCollins Publishers.

"Elevator" by Lucille Clifton is reprinted by permission of Curtis Brown, Ltd. Copyright ©1992 by Lucille Clifton.

"Go Home" by Janet Reed McFatter is reprinted from *A Green Place*, compiled by William Jay Smith, by permission of Curtis Brown, Ltd.

"A Boy and a Mountain" from *Banner in the Sky* by James Ramsey Ullman, copyright 1954, is reprinted by permission of HarperCollins Publishers.

"Valentine for Earth" by Frances Frost, is reprinted from *The Little Naturalist*, copyright © 1959 by the Estate of Frances Frost and Kurt Werth.

"All Summer in a Day" by Ray Bradbury copyright 1954, renewed ©1982 by Ray Bradbury is reprinted by permission of Don Coglin Associates, Inc.

ILLUSTRATION

14-32 Alex Cerveny; 46-51 K. Boake W.; 100-101 *background* Russell Ganzi; 101 *tl* Charis Yousefian; 101 *bl* Alex Camelio; 101 *tr* Julia Keller; 101 *br* Rebecca Rogers.

PHOTOGRAPHY

4 *t* Julie Bidwell/©D.C. Heath; *b* H. Gans/The Image Works; 5 Museum of the City of New York. The J. Clarence Davies Collection; 6 *b* R.M. Collins/The Image Works; 8-9 Bob Brudd/Tony Stone Images; 8 *inset* Bob Thomason/Tony Stone Images; 9 *inset* Dan Derdula; 10 *t* Julie Bidwell/©D.C. Heath; *b* John Owens/©D.C. Heath; 11 *t* Steve & Mary Skjold Photographs; *c* John Owens/©D.C. Heath; *b* J. Berndt/Stock Boston; 12-13 Jon Nickson; 13 *inset* Photo by Carlo Ontal/Courtesy of Harcourt Brace & Company; 33 Photo by Jill Paton Walsh/Courtesy of Harper Collins Publishers; 34-35 John Kelly/The Image Bank; 35 *inset* Rob Atkins/The Image Bank; 38-39 Russ Davies/The Image Bank; 42 Ira Block/The Image Bank; 43 *t* Bob Atkins/The Image Bank; *b* Paul Carl; 44-45 Russ Davies/The Image Bank; 44 *inset l* Gayna Hoffmann; 45 *inset t* Earle D. Lyon/Courtesy of the Caxton Printers, Ltd.; *inset b* Gayna Hoffmann; 52 Jeff Spielman/The Image Bank; 55 The Bettmann Archive; 56 Culver Pictures; 56-57 *background* The Bettmann Archive; 58-59, 60-61 Culver Pictures; 62 Museum of the City of New York. The J. Clarence Davies Collection; 66 Sarah Conrad/Courtesy of Harper Collins Publishers; 66-67 Robert Kristofik/The Image Bank; 68 New Jersey State Museum Collection, Trenton NJ; 69 Courtesy of Harper Collins Publishing; 70 Richard Hamilton Smith; 71 Courtesy of Macmillan Children's Book Group; 72-73 Arthur Meyerson/The Image Bank; 73 Courtesy of Henry Holt & Company; 74 Hood Museum of Art, Dartmouth College, Hanover, NH. Gift of the artist, through the friends of the Library. ©Maxfield Parrish/VAGA NY 1995; 76 Paul Trummer/The Image Bank; 77 Steve Elmore/The Stock Market; 78-79 Jeff Adamo/The Stock Market; 81 Lynn M. Stone/The Image Bank; 83 Zefa-DAMM/The Stock Market; 86-87 David Ball/The Stock Market; 89 Courtesy of Harold Matson Company, Inc.; 90, 93, 95, 97 The Menil Collection, Houston. ©1995 ARS, NY/SPADEM/ADAGP, Paris. Photo: Janet Woodard; 98-99 Richard Zeisler Collection, New York. ©1995 ARS, NY/SPADEM/ADAGP, Paris; 99 UPI/Bettmann Newsphotos; 105 Nancy Sheehan/©D.C. Heath; 106 *t* Jeff H. Dunn/Stock Boston; 106 *b* Wm. S. Nawrocki/Nawrocki Stock Photo, Inc.; 110-111 Steve Bittinger; 112 Elizabeth Crews/Stock Boston; 113 Ken O'Donoghue/©D.C. Heath; 114 Jeff Greenberg/PhotoEdit; 115 K.O.P.E. **Back cover** *t* Richard Haynes/©D.C. Heath; *c* Julie Bidwell/©D.C. Heath; *b* John Owens/©D.C. Heath.

Full Pronunciation Key for Footnoted Words

(Each pronunciation and definition is adapted from *Scott, Foresman Advanced Dictionary* by E.L. Thorndike and Clarence L. Barnhart.)

The pronunciation of each footnoted word is shown just after the word, in this way: **abbreviate** [ə brē′ vē āt]. The letters and signs used are pronounced as in the words below. The mark ′ is placed after a syllable with primary or heavy accent, as in the example above. The mark ′ after a syllable shows a secondary or lighter accent, as in **abbreviation** [ə brē′ vē ā′ shən].

Some words, taken from foreign languages, are spoken with sounds that do not otherwise occur in English. Symbols for these sounds are given in the key as "foreign sounds."

a	hat, cap	j	jam, enjoy	u	cup, butter	**foreign sounds**
ā	age, face	k	kind, seek	u̇	full, put	Y as in French *du*.
ä	father, far	l	land, coal	ü	rule, move	Pronounce (ē) with
		m	me, am	v	very, save	the lips rounded as
b	bad, rob	n	no, in	w	will, woman	for (ü).
ch	child, much	ng	long, bring	y	young, yet	
d	did, red			z	zero, breeze	à as in French *ami*.
		o	hot, rock	zh	measure, seizure	Pronounce (ä) with
e	let, best	ō	open, go			the lips spread and
ē	equal, be	ô	order, all	ə represents:		held tense.
ėr	term, learn	oi	oil, voice		a in about	
		ou	house, out		e in taken	œ as in French *peu*.
f	fat, if				i in pencil	Pronounce (ā) with
g	go, bag	p	paper, cup		o in lemon	the lips rounded as for (ō).
h	he, how	r	run, try		u in circus	
		s	say, yes			N as in French *bon*.
i	it, pin	sh	she, rush			The N is not pro-
ī	ice, five	t	tell, it			nounced, but shows
		th	thin, both			that the vowel before
		ᵺH	then, smooth			it is nasal.

H as in German *ach*. Pronounce (k) without closing the breath passage.